Awesome Addition
and
Super Subtraction

Authors
AIMS Research Fellows
David Mitchell, Coordinator

Illustrator
David Schlotterback

Editor
Betty Cordel

Desktop Publisher
Tracey Lieder
Leticia Rivera

Acknowledgment

Our thanks to Christina Johnson for writing the activity *Making Arrangements*.

CURR
QA
115
.M57
2004

ISBN **1-881431-99-1**
Printed in the United States of America

Table of Contents

Building Conceptual Understanding

Making Number/Operations Boards 3

Building on Base 7

Base Place (The Pluses) 10

Base Place (The Minuses) 13

Hopping on Base 16

Basic Beans 20

Money Has its Place 30

Meaningful Problem Solving

Shape Frame Math 38

Making Arrangements 42

Math Spots 44

Diving into Diffies 60

Digits in Disguise 64

Uncle Rebus Stories 70

Playful and Intelligent Practice

Cornering the Facts 86

Hands on the Addition and Subtraction Table 91

Make it Even 93

Base Ten Bingo 101

Blockout 107

Who Has? Addition and Subtraction 113

I Hear and I Forget,

I See and
I Remember,

I Do and I Understand.

Chinese Proverb

A Model of Mathematics and Operations

The learning experiences in *Awesome Addition and Super Subtraction* make use of the four learning environments embodied in the Model of Mathematics. The goal for students is to understand these two whole-number operations, and to this end students must be engaged in all four environments.

Doing

The circle represents hands-on experiences that include the use of manipulatives and models. Students will use manipulatives that help them internalize the meaning of addition and subtraction. It is of critical importance that students understand these operations at the concrete level.

Illustrating

The square symbolizes the picturing of information. It is often an important avenue for students to "picture" in the mind the meaning behind the operations. Students are given opportunity to interpret picture models of addition and subtraction as well as to draw their own.

A Model of Mathematics

- Real World Manipulative — Doing
- Counting / Measuring
- Number Abstract — Writing
- Graph Representational — Illustrating
- Generalizing Formula Abstract — Thinking — $N = ?$

Writing

The triangle represents addition and subtraction at an abstract level. It includes the use of symbols and numerals. The experiences in *Awesome Addition and Super Subtraction* make strong connections between the real-world circle experiences and the abstraction of the triangle. This connection will give insight into the meaning of addition and subtraction.

Thinking

The fourth learning environment is represented by the hexagon. The hexagon challenges students to reflect on the operations and to apply that knowledge to new learning situations.

The best learning experiences are those that make good use of all four environments. The use of this learning model will provide rich learning experiences.

Building Conceptual Understanding

Addition

Concrete/Manipulative Level

At this level students join sets of objects in order to experience the basic operation in a concrete way.

Using countable objects

With *countable* objects, such as beans or buttons, the addition operation consists of joining two or more sets to form one set. Usually the sets have an unequal number of objects, but it is not a requirement. At the *manipulative* stage, students construct sets of countable objects, and then join or combine those sets into one. The move to combine the sets into one is referred to as the operation of addition. By counting, students can determine the number of objects in each set and also in the combined set—confirming that no objects have been added or lost in the transaction.

 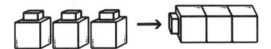

Using measured objects

Objects that have an attribute of length, such as Unifix cubes or straws, are appropriate for a *measured* model for addition. The addition of lengths consists of placing straws or Unifix cubes end to end so that one length is an extension of the other. Each length can be measured in units such as number of cubes or number of centimeters or inches.

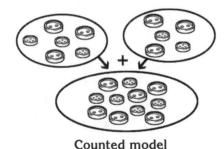

Representational/Pictorial Level

At the *representational* level, sometimes called the connecting stage, objects and actions are represented or depicted by pictures or diagrams. For addition, each set is pictured and arrows indicate that the sets have been combined into one.

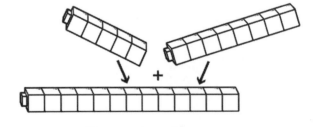

Counted model   Measured model

Abstract/Symbolic Level

At this level numerals, symbols, and relationship signs are used to represent the objects and actions of the concrete and representative levels. At the *symbolic* stage, objects can be counted and recorded symbolically with a plus (+) sign to represent the combination or union of sets. The equal (=) sign shows that no objects were gained or lost in the process. Thus the mathematical sentence $6 + 5 = 11$ has meaning that can be reconstructed with manipulatives or translated in pictures. In the measured model, the plus (+) sign then represents the process of extending the length or building a train of Unifix cubes or straws.

Six and five is eleven.   Five plus eight is thirteen.

$6 + 5 = 11$ $5 + 8 = 13$

Building Conceptual Understanding

Subtraction

Concrete/Manipulative Level

At this level students separate a subset of objects from a larger set or compare two sets of objects, frequently unequal sets, in one-to-one correspondence.

Using countable objects

With countable objects such as nuts and bolts, two kinds of experiences at the manipulative level may be explored—subtraction by separation or by comparison. In the separating model, students construct a set of objects and then separate or "take away" some (occasionally all) of the objects, and count the remaining objects to determine the difference. In the comparison model, students match two sets of objects in one-to-one correspondence to determine relationships such as more than, less than, or equal to.

Using measurable objects

With objects that have a property that can be measured such as length, the separating model consists of building a train of cubes or nuts and then breaking the train into two parts and removing or separating one part to determine the length of the remaining part. A comparison model similarly matches two trains of blocks in one-to-one correspondence to determine a relationship of more than, less than, or equal to.

Representational/Pictorial Level

At the representational level, sometimes called the connecting stage, objects and actions are represented or depicted by pictures or diagrams. For subtraction, a set is pictured and arrows indicate that a set has been separated into two parts or that two sets have been compared by matching elements in one-to-one correspondence.

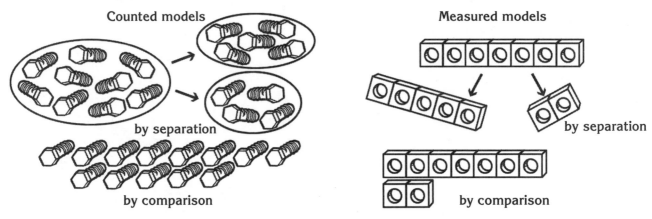

Abstract/Symbolic Level

At this level, numerals, symbols, and relationship signs are used to represent objects and actions of the concrete and representational levels. At the symbolic level, objects can be counted and recorded symbolically with a minus (–) sign to represent the separation of one set from another. The equal (=) sign shows that no objects were lost or gained in the process and that the sum of the parts equals the whole.

Nine objects take away five objects = four objects

$$9 - 5 = 4$$

Nine objects compared to five objects:

Nine objects are four more than five objects. $9 > 5$ or $9 - 5 = 4$

Five objects are four less than nine. $5 < 9$ or $9 - 5 = 4$

Making Sense of Whole Number Operations

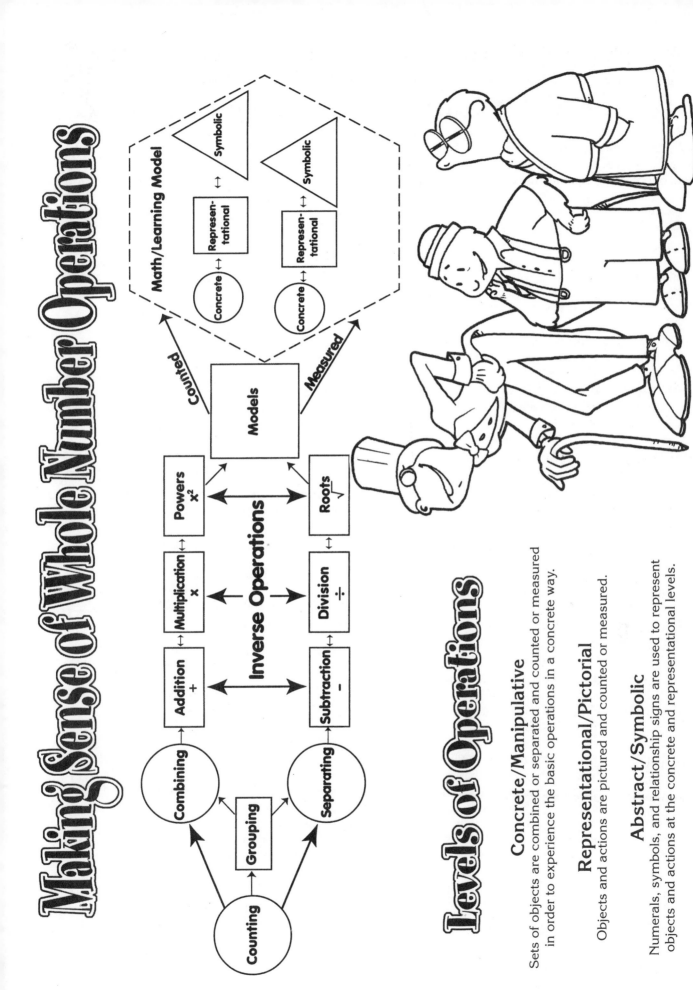

Math/Learning Model

Concrete ↔ Representational ↔ Symbolic

Concrete ↔ Representational ↔ Symbolic

Models

Counted

Measured

Powers x^2 ↔ Multiplication $\times$ ↔ Addition $+$

Roots $\sqrt{}$ ↔ Division $\div$ ↔ Subtraction $-$

Inverse Operations

Combining

Separating

Grouping

Counting

Levels of Operations

Concrete/Manipulative
Sets of objects are combined or separated and counted or measured in order to experience the basic operations in a concrete way.

Representational/Pictorial
Objects and actions are pictured and counted or measured.

Abstract/Symbolic
Numerals, symbols, and relationship signs are used to represent objects and actions at the concrete and representational levels.

Making Sense of Whole Number Operations

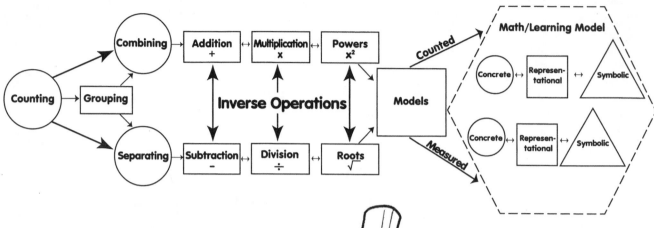

Levels of Operations

Concrete/Manipulative
Sets of objects are combined or separated and counted or measured in order to experience the basic operations in a concrete way.

Representational/Pictorial
Objects and actions are pictured and counted or measured.

Abstract/Symbolic
Numerals, symbols, and relationship signs are used to represent objects and actions at the concrete and representational levels.

Introduction

Traditionally the teaching of number concepts *begins* with introducing students to arithmetic through numerals and symbols. What elementary students need most is to make *meaning* of number and the basic operations through the use of concrete manipulatives and then make connections between the mathematics they study at the concrete level and the numerals and symbols at the abstract level. The difficulties that many children have with mathematics, specifically the potential for computational errors, are due in large part to their inability to make sense of the numeric symbols and the connection of any meaning to the algorithm.

The accompanying diagram speaks to us about a view of arithmetic that deals with groups. Students enter school and begin to learn to count by recognizing a one-to-one correspondence between an object and a number. Soon they recognize the number of objects in small groups without having to count each one. It is this recognition of groups that paves the way for considering each of the operations as one of combining or of separating groups of objects. Addition, multiplication, and raising to a power are all examples of a process of combining or joining while subtraction, division, and extracting a root are examples of a process of separating or partitioning. Each of the basic operations should be experienced at a variety of levels.

Beyond Understanding — The Basic Facts

A balanced mathematics program includes frequent doses of *playful*, *intelligent practice,* and *creative, real-world problem-solving* experiences that provide opportunity to apply the basic operations.

Making Number/Operation Boards

In much of the study of place value, students will need to use *Number/Operation Boards*. These are boards on which students can manipulate objects, group them, add and subtract, and connect values to the places numbers occupy. These boards can be ordered from AIMS or you can construct you own.

Number/Operation Boards are constructed using the same pieces of construction paper. *Number Boards* will be on one side and *Operations Boards* will be on the other side.

1. To build a set of *Number/ Operation Boards,* use 12" x 18" pieces of construction paper in yellow and blue and green.
   The yellow sheet will always be used for the ones place, the blue sheet will always be used for the tens place (numbers to 99), and the green will always be used for the hundreds place (numbers to 999).
2. You will need to prepare one set of boards per student.
3. One side of each paper will be left blank. This is the *Number Board* side. The *Number Boards* will be used to teach the grouping of objects into sets of tens and hundreds.
4. On the other side of the paper, draw lines with a black marker to divide the paper into thirds along the 18" dimension. Add strips of pink paper to the bottom third of each paper to show the division of part-part-whole.
5. Laminate these sheets of construction paper for durablity.
6. *Place Value Labels* can be added.

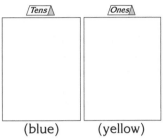

Number Boards with labels: tens and ones

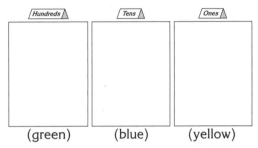

Number Boards with labels: hundreds, tens, and ones

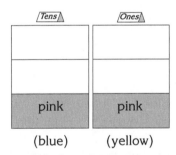

Operation Boards with labels: tens and ones

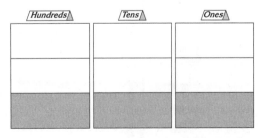

Operation Boards with labels: hundreds, tens, and ones

Hundreds	Tens	Ones

Hundreds	Tens	Ones

Hundreds	Tens	Ones

Place Value Labels

Topic
Place Value

Learning Goals
The students will
1. construct buildings or designs using Base Ten Blocks, and
2. calculate the value of each building or design.

Guiding Document
NCTM Standards 2000*
- *Count with understanding and recognize "how many" in sets of objects*
- *Use multiple models to develop initial understandings of place value and the base-ten number system*
- *Connect number words and numerals to the quantities they represent, using various physical models and representations*
- *Understand the effects of adding and subtracting whole numbers*

Math
Number sense and numeration

Integrated Processes
Observing
Classifying
Comparing and contrasting

Materials
For each group of four students:
- *Place Value Labels* (see *Management 3*)
- two *Number Boards* (see *Management 4*)
- Base Ten Blocks
- student record sheet

Background Information
Students need time to explore the Base Ten Blocks. This activity provides an opportunity to construct "buildings" or designs and then asks the students to find the value of what they built.

The Base Ten Blocks used in this activity show a proportional relationship. The longs are ten times larger than the units, and the flats are tens times larger than the longs. Ones are clearly smaller and the hundreds are clearly larger. These blocks reflect a clear relationship for ones, tens, and hundreds. The units, representations of ones, can be grouped to make a long. The longs, representations of tens, can

be exchanged for units. These experiences help the students develop a sense of the value of each place and each piece.

The grouping and exchanging that takes place with the Base Ten Blocks provide opportunity for the students to develop an understanding of the value of the place as well as the value of the face of the digits. A collection of three longs and four units would be displayed as three tens and four ones and would have a face value of 34.

Management
1. It is assumed that the students have had prior grouping experiences in which the idea of each place holding only nine units or sets has been developed.
2. The focus is on exploration of the materials.
3. Duplicate two sets of *Place Value Labels* for each student group.
4. Each pair of students will need a three-section (ones, tens and hundreds—yellow, blue, and green) *Number/Operation Board*.

Procedure
1. Ask the *Key Questions* and state the *Learning Goals*.
2. Distribute a set of Base Ten Blocks to each group of students.
3. Ask the students to open the box of materials and remove one block of each size.
4. Challenge the students to find the value of each of the pieces if the unit is equal to one. (The students should discover and describe that the long is equal to ten and the flat is equal to 100.) Direct a discussion in how the students arrived at the value of each of the pieces.
5. Direct the students to create a design or building with the Base Ten Blocks.
6. Distribute the *Number Boards* and *Place Value Labels* to each student pair.
7. Direct the students to use the number side of the boards. Tell them that they will be decomposing (disassembling) their designs/buildings in order to find their values. Explain that the students will be placing the units, longs, and flats into the appropriate sections of the *Number Boards*. (Color, position, and label indicate the value of each place. The Base Ten Blocks are being used in this activity as single objects in their placement. The unit on the ones board represents **one** unit, the long on the tens board represents

one ten, and the flat on the hundreds board represents **one** hundred. The board represents the value while the Base Ten Blocks serve only to reinforce the placement.)

8. Remind students that only nine of each piece can be on the boards. Tell them that if it is necessary they can trade units for longs and longs for flats.
9. Have the students share the value of their building or design.
10. Distribute the student sheet. Have students work through the problems.

Connecting Learning

1. Why do you think the units, longs, and flats have different values?
2. Why was it important to discover the value of the pieces?
3. What would the value of ten flats be?
4. What limited the size of the building or design?
5. How big would a design or building be that had a value of six? What about a value of 600?
6. What did you learn by doing this activity?

Evidence of Learning

1. Listen for student explanation during the *Reflecting on Learning* questions as well as discussion during the activity. Students need to be able to tell the value of each place as well as the value of each piece. The cubes represent ones, the rods represent tens, and the flats represent hundreds. The students need to explain that each column has a value based on position. The first column on the right represents the ones place, the second column represents the tens, and the third column represents the hundreds place.
2. Look for accurate trading and calculating of value of the building or design. Students should be able to tell the value of the building with the concrete materials as well as the written record.

* Reprinted with permission from *Principles and Standards for School Mathematics,* 2000 by the National Council of Teachers of Mathematics. All rights reserved.

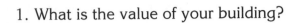

building on base

1. What is the value of your building?

_____
Value

2. Design a building using three flats, seven longs, and two units.

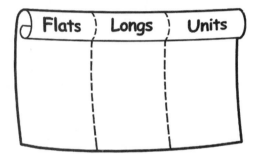

Flats	Longs	Units

What is its value?

_____
Value

3. What is the value of a building that has two flats, five longs, and 14 units?

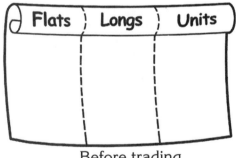

Flats	Longs	Units

Before trading

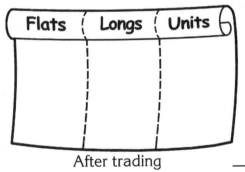

Flats	Longs	Units

After trading

_____
Value

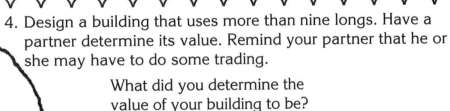

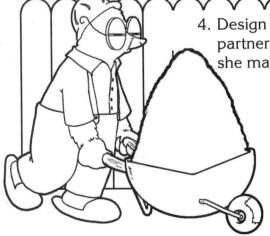

4. Design a building that uses more than nine longs. Have a partner determine its value. Remind your partner that he or she may have to do some trading.

What did you determine the value of your building to be?

_____
Value

What did your partner determine its value to be?

} Explain any differences on the back of this paper.

_____
Value

Topic
Whole Number Operations, Addition

Learning Goals
The students will:
1. construct manipulative models to represent operations of addition, using one-, two-, and three-digit numbers; and
2. solve two- and three-digit addition problems with and without regrouping.

Guiding Document
NCTM Standards 2000*
- *Count with understanding and recognize "how many" in sets of objects*
- *Use multiple models to develop initial understandings of place value and the base-ten number system*
- *Connect number words and numerals to the quantities they represent, using various physical models and representations*
- *Understand the effects of adding and subtracting whole numbers*

Math
Number sense and numeration
Whole number operations
Place value
Expanded notation

Integrated Processes
Observing
Classifying
Comparing and contrasting

Materials
For each group of four students:
　Place Value Labels (see *Management 3*)
　two *Number/Operation Boards* (see *Management 4*)
　Base Ten Blocks
　yellow, green, blue, and pink sticky notes, 3" x 3"
　　(see *Management 5*)

Background Information
　The Base Ten Blocks used in this series of activities show a proportional relationship. The longs are ten times larger than the cubes, and the flats are tens times larger than the longs. These blocks reflect a clear relationship for ones, tens, and hundreds. The cubes (the ones) can be grouped to make a long. The longs can be exchanged for cubes. These experiences help the students develop a sense of the value of each place. Ones are clearly smaller and the hundreds are clearly larger.

　The grouping and exchanging that take place with the base ten materials provides opportunity for the students to develop an understanding of the value of the place as well as the face value of the digits. A collection of three longs and four cubes would be displayed as 3 tens and 4 ones and would have a face value of 34.

　The sticky notes used to record the numbers on the *Operation Boards* will provide for an opportunity to informally explore expanded notion.

Management
1. It is assumed that the students have had prior grouping experiences in which the idea of each place holding only nine units or sets has been developed.
2. This activity should be spread out over several days.
3. Duplicate two sets of *Place Value Labels* for each student group.
4. Each pair of students will need a three-section (ones, tens, and hundreds—yellow, blue, and green) *Number/Operation Board*. They will use the *Operation* side of the board for this activity. It is the side that is divided into three sections.
5. The sticky notes will be used to record the addition problems. The colors match the colors on the *Number/Operation Boards*.

Procedure
Part One—Addition Without Regrouping
1. Give the students yellow, blue, and green *Operation Boards, Place Value Labels*, and Base Ten Blocks. Direct them to position the boards with the pink section at the bottom. The yellow represents the ones place. The blue represents the tens place, and the green represents the hundreds place. Ask them to place *ones, tens, and hundreds* labels above the appropriate boards. (Color, position, and label indicate the value of each place. The Base Ten Blocks, although proportional in their value and used in that manner in *Building on Base*, are being used in this activity as single objects in their placement. The unit on the ones board represents **one** unit, the long on the tens board represents **one** ten, and the flat on the hundreds board represents **one** hundred. The board represents the value while the Base Ten Blocks serve only to reinforce the placement.)

2. Present a number problem for the class to solve. Example: There are 17 boys and 12 girls in the class. How many students are in the class altogether?

3. Direct the students to place longs and cubes in the top section of their *Operation Boards* to represent the number of boys in the class. Ask them to name the number in terms of tens and ones. [1 ten and 7 ones]

4. Tell them to place longs and cubes in the middle section of their *Operation Boards* to represent the number of girls in the class. Ask them to name the number in terms of tens and ones. [1 ten and 2 ones]

5. To find the solution to the question "How many students are in the class altogether?" have the students combine the longs and cubes from the top two sections into the pink bottom sections of the *Operation Boards*. Ask them to name the number in terms of tens and ones. [2 tens and 9 ones] Have them name the number as a total. [29 students altogether]

6. On the chalkboard, record the number sentence as $17 + 12 = 29$. Explain that this + sign tells them to combine all the longs and cubes.

7. Continue presenting number problems in this manner, being careful not to require the students to regroup at this time. Add number problems that require the use of the flats (hundreds) if your students are ready for them.

Part Two—Addition With Regrouping
1. Give each student a yellow, blue, and green *Operation Board*. Direct them to position the boards with the pink section at the bottom.

2. Write nine on the chalkboard. Tell the students to build this number on the top section of the ones (yellow) *Operation Board*. Check to make sure the students have placed the cubes on the appropriate sections and boards.

3. Direct the students to place their tens place (blue) *Operation Boards* next to and to the left of their yellow boards.

4. Write +7 on the board and tell them to place seven cubes in the middle section of their yellow board. Check to make sure the students placed the cubes on the appropriate sections and boards.

5. Present a number sentence such as: There were nine children playing soccer. Seven more children joined them. How many children were there altogether?

6. Have the students build the solution to this number sentence on their boards. Pause, waiting for someone in the group to possibly determine that they have a set of ten ones. Ask them what they think they should do with the set of ten. [Trade it in for a long and move the long over to the tens (blue) board.] If they do not think of this on their own, direct them to make this move. Have them move their cubes to represent the sum or total to the bottom pink section of their boards. Check to make sure the students have placed one long and six cubes in the appropriate places on their boards. Ask the students to name the number that represents the solution to the question. [16 children playing soccer or one ten and six ones]

7. Continue presenting additional number problems that require the students to regroup. Use higher numbers such as $28 + 36$, $116 + 35$, and $236 + 127$.

Part Three—Addition Without Regrouping Recorded
1. Explain that students will be using the same type of board they have been using, but now they will include sticky notes to record the numbers they have built.

2. Using longs and cubes, direct the students to build the number 37 on their boards. Ask the students to name the number of tens represented. [3] ...ones. [7]

3. Ask the students to place sticky notes on these boards, matching colors of sticky notes to colors of boards. Tell them to record the number 7 on the yellow sticky notes and a 30 on the blue sticky notes. Discuss how these numbers represent the number of ones and sets of tens located on their boards.

4. In the middle section of the boards, have the students build the number 31. Ask the students to name the number of tens and ones represented. Direct them to write 30 and 1 on the appropriate sticky notes.

5. Present a number story such as: On Monday, there were 37 tickets sold for a concert. On Tuesday, 31 more tickets were sold. How many tickets were sold altogether?

6. Direct the students to build the solution to the question on their boards. Check for appropriate grouping in the tens and ones places on the boards. Ask the students to name and record the solution to the question on the sticky notes. [60 and 8]

7. Tell the students to remove the sticky notes and stack them on each other and sequence them as an addition problem.

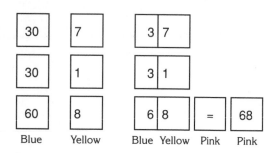

Blue   Yellow   Blue Yellow Pink   Pink

8. Ask the students to read the numbers as in the number sentence. [37 + 31 = 68]

9. Direct the students to add a plus sign and add an equal sign to the problem.

Part Four—Addition With Regrouping Recorded

1. Using the *Operation Boards* and sticky notes, tell the students to build and record 129 in the top sections and 163 in the middle sections of their boards.

2. Present a number problem such as: In the morning, there were 129 students present at the soccer clinic. In the afternoon, 163 more students joined the clinic. How many students attended the clinic altogether?

3. Give the students a pink sticky note on which to record the + sign. Have them place the plus sign to the left of the *Operation Board.*

4. Tell them to combine the cubes in the ones place and to move them to the pink portion of the boards. Ask them to name the number of ones. Point out that they have a set of ten and that they will need to trade these for a long.

5. Direct them to bring the long up to the top portion of the tens place and to record a small one above the two on the sticky note to show that they have added a set of ten. Tell them the small one is a way of reminding them that they have regrouped the ones into a set of ten. Instruct them to name and record the number of ones in the ones box at the bottom of their boards.

6. Have the students bring all the sets of ten down to the lower part of the board. Tell them to name and record the total number of sets of ten on a pink sticky note at the bottom. Direct them to do the same with the flats in the hundreds place.

7. Direct the students to remove the sticky notes and to line them up at the bottom of the boards. Ask the students to name the number written in the bottom recording boxes. [292]

8. Repeat this procedure with several other number combinations that require regrouping.

Connecting Learning

1. How did you decide how many objects to put in each section of your boards?

2. What do you need to do when you have more than nine cubes in the ones place?

3. What does the symbol + tell you to do?

4. Build a number story on your board and then write the number story using numerals. Tell your story to the class.

5. How did the *Operation Boards* help you solve addition problems?

6. In your own words, tell what place value means.

Evidence of Learning

1. Listen for student explanation during the *Reflecting on Learning* questions as well as discussion during the activity. The students need to be able to explain why they need to regroup numbers as they add. The students should also be able to tell that addition is a part-part-whole relationship. [2 frogs + 3 frogs = 5 frogs: 2 frogs is a part, 3 frogs is a part, and 5 frogs is the whole]

2. Look for accurate recording and building of the numbers on the *Operation Boards*. The students need to show that the cubes are placed on the ones boards and in the ones columns, the longs on the tens boards and the tens columns, and the flats on the hundreds boards and the hundreds columns.

*   Reprinted with permission from *Principles and Standards for School Mathematics,* 2000 by the National Council of Teachers of Mathematics. All rights reserved.

Topic
Whole Number Operations, Subtraction

Learning Goals
The students will:
1. construct manipulative models to represent operations of subtraction, using one-, two-, and three-digit numbers; and
2. model and solve subtraction story problems with and without regrouping.

Guiding Document
NCTM Standards 2000*
- *Count with understanding and recognize "how many" in sets of objects*
- *Use multiple models to develop initial understandings of place value and the base-ten number system*
- *Connect number words and numerals to the quantities they represent, using various physical models and representations*
- *Understand the effects of adding and subtracting whole numbers*

Math
Number sense and numeration
Whole number operations
Place value
Expanded notation

Integrated Processes
Observing
Classifying
Comparing and contrasting

Materials
For each group of four students:
Place Value Labels (see *Management 3*)
two *Number/Operation Boards* (see *Management 4*)
Base Ten Blocks
student recording sheet

Background Information
The Base Ten Blocks used in this series of activities show a proportional relationship. The longs are ten times larger than the cubes, and the flats are tens times larger than the longs. These blocks reflect a clear relationship for ones, tens, and hundreds. The cubes (the ones) can be grouped to make a long. The longs can be exchanged for cubes. These experiences help the students develop a sense of the value of each place. Ones are clearly smaller and the hundreds are clearly larger.

The grouping and exchanging that take place with the base ten materials provide opportunity for the students to develop an understanding of the value of the place as well as the face value of the digits. A collection of three longs and four cubes would be displayed as 3 tens and 4 ones and would have a face value of 34.

The recording sheet reinforces the concept of place value and subtraction. It also more closely matches the traditional algorithm while attaching it to a model.

Management
1. It is assumed that the students have had prior grouping experiences in which the idea of each place holding only nine units or sets has been developed.
2. This activity should be spread out over several weeks.
3. Duplicate two sets of *Place Value Labels* for each student group.
4. Each pair of students will need a three-section (ones, tens, and hundreds—yellow, blue, and green) *Number/Operation Board*. They will use the *Operation* side (the side divided into thirds) throughout the activity.
5. Make sure the students are solving problems that relate to stories. It is of little value to simply add or subtract numbers.
6. The student recording sheet is designed to help the students keep the digits in the correct columns as well as offer them a written record of what they are manipulating on the *Operation Boards*.

Procedure
Part One—Subtraction Without Regrouping
1. Give the students yellow, blue, and green *Operation Boards, Place Value Labels*, and Base Ten Blocks. Direct students to position the boards with the pink section at the top. The yellow represents the ones place. The blue represents the tens place, and the green represents the hundreds place. Ask them to place *ones, tens,* and *hundreds* labels above the appropriate boards. (Color, position and label indicate the value of each place. The Base Ten Blocks, although proportional in their value and used in that manner in *Building on Base*, are

being used in this activity as single objects in their placement. The unit on the ones board represents **one** unit, the long on the tens board represents **one** ten, and the flat on the hundreds board represents **one** hundred. The board represents the value while the Base Ten Blocks serve only to reinforce the placement.)

2. Present a number problem for the class to solve such as: Nick had 15 action figures. He gave his brother Andrew 3 of them. How many did Nick have left?

3. Direct the students to place longs and cubes in the top pink section of their *Operation Boards* to represent the number of action figures Nick had. Write 15 on the chalkboard and then write minus three below it. Ask the students what the minus sign represents in this story. [The fact that Nick is giving away something.]

4. Tell the students to move three cubes from the 15 into the middle section of the yellow board. Discuss what this number of cubes represents. [These cubes represent the action figures Nick has given away.] Tell students to move the longs and cubes that are left in the pink section all the way down to the bottom sections.

5. Repeat this with two- and three-digit problems until the students have developed a sense of whole-part-part for subtraction. Be sure to select numbers that do not require regrouping.

6. Discuss with the students how subtraction and addition are related. Direct them to turn the boards around to check a subtraction problem. If their sum matches the original number they began with in their subtraction problem, they can assume their subtraction answer is correct.

Part Two—Subtraction With Regrouping

1. The students will now do another kind of subtraction problem.

2. Present the following problem to the students: Charlie scored 23 points in a basketball game. Mary scored 9 points. How many more points did Charlie score? Write the number sentence on the board 23 – 9 = ?

3. Ask the students what they will need to place in the pink section of their *Operation Boards* to represent 23? Make sure the students place two longs on the blue board and three cubes on the yellow board.

4. Ask the students to take away nine cubes from the ones section to represent the number of points Mary scored. Pause and wait while the students determine how to remove the nine cubes. Ask them how they think they can solve the problem. Guide them in trading one of the longs for ten cubes. Place the ten cubes with the three original cubes. The students will then be able to move nine cubes into the middle section of the board.

5. Work the problem on the chalkboard by crossing out the two in the tens place and adding a one above the two in the tens place. Add a small ten above the three indicating 13 in the ones place. Discuss how there are now 13 cubes temporarily in the ones place.

6. Continue working with additional problems that require regrouping using two- and three-digit problems.

Part Three—Recording Subtraction With and Without Regrouping

1. Distribute the recording sheets. Select a problem for the students to solve.

2. Direct the students to solve the problem on the *Operation Boards* as they also record the problem and solve it on the recording sheet. Point out that they will need to place the digits for the problem in the correct place on the recording sheet.

Connecting Learning

1. How did you decide how many objects to put in each section of your boards?

2. What do you need to do when you have more than nine cubes in the ones place?

3. What does the symbol – tell you to do?

4. Build a number story on your board and then write the number story using numerals. Tell your story to the class.

5. How did the *Operation Board* help you solve subtraction problems? How did the recording sheet help you in solving the problems?

6. In your own words, tell what place value means.

Evidence of Learning

1. Listen for understanding as students explain the whole-part-part relationship.

2. Listen for accuracy as students explain the need for regrouping.

3. Look for accurate recording and building of the numbers.

* Reprinted with permission from *Principles and Standards for School Mathematics*, 2000 by the National Council of Teachers of Mathematics. All rights reserved.

Operations Board

1	hundreds	tens	ones

2	hundreds	tens	ones

3	hundreds	tens	ones

4			

5			

6			

7			

8			

9			

Purpose of the Game
Students will explore different bases

Materials
For each group of two students:
    number die (see *Management 1*)
    Hopping on Base mat
    frog markers (see *Management 2*)
    tally sheet

Management
1. Prepare three different die. The first will have zeros, ones, and twos on the faces of the cube. The second will have ones, twos, and threes on the faces. The third can have any numbers as long as the highest number is less than ten.
2. Prepare a set of frog markers in the three different colors: yellow, blue, and green.
3. Copy three lily pads for each group.

The Frog Choruses
The Frog Trio
Rules
1. The object of the game is to get three green frogs onto the third lily pad in the fewest number of rolls of the number die.
2. Begin play by rolling the number die with the zeros, ones, and twos on it. The number that is rolled tells how many yellow frogs are to be placed on the first lily pad.
3. Keep a tally of each roll of the die on the tally sheet.
4. Once three yellow frogs are on the first lily pad, the pad is full. These three frogs can then be traded for a single blue frog that can be placed on the second lily pad. The second lily pad is full when there are three blue frogs on it. These three blue frogs can be traded for a green frog that is then placed on the third lily pad.
5. The frog trio is complete when you have three green frogs on the third lily pad.

The Frog Quintet
Rules
1. The object of the game is to get five green frogs onto the third lily pad in the fewest number of rolls of the number die.

2. Begin play by rolling the number die with the ones, twos, and threes on it. The number rolled tells how many yellow frogs are to be placed on the first lily pad.
3. Keep a tally of each roll of the die on the tally sheet.
4. Once five yellow frogs are on the first lily pad, the pad is full. These five frogs can then be traded for a single blue frog that can be placed on the second lily pad. The second lily pad is full when there are five blue frogs on it. These five blue frogs can be traded for a green frog that is then placed on the third lily pad.
5. The frog quintet is complete when you have five green frogs on the third lily pad.

The Frog Ensemble
Rules
1. The object of the game is to get ten green frogs onto the third lily pad in the fewest number of rolls of the number die.
2. Begin play by rolling the third number die. The number that rolled tells how many yellow frogs are to be placed on the first lily pad.
3. Keep a tally of each roll of the die on the tally sheet.
4. Once ten yellow frogs are on the first lily pad, the pad is full. These ten frogs can then be traded for a single blue frog that can be placed on the second lily pad. The second lily pad is full when there are ten blue frogs on it. These ten blue frogs can be traded for a green frog that is then placed on the third lily pad.
5. The frog ensemble is complete when you have ten green frogs on the third lily pad.

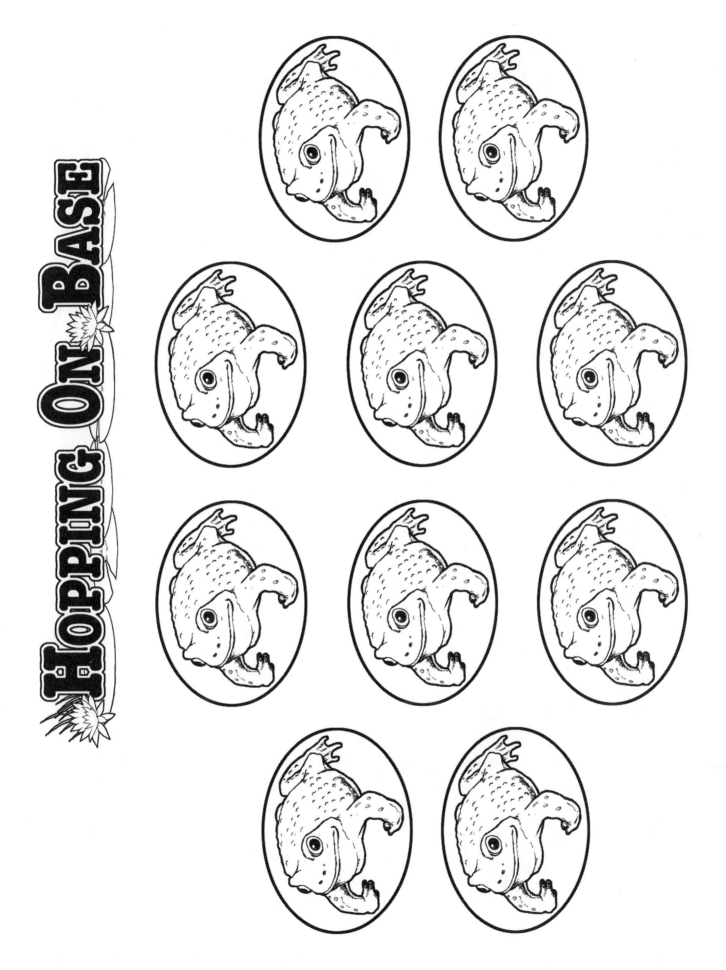

18

Tally Sheet

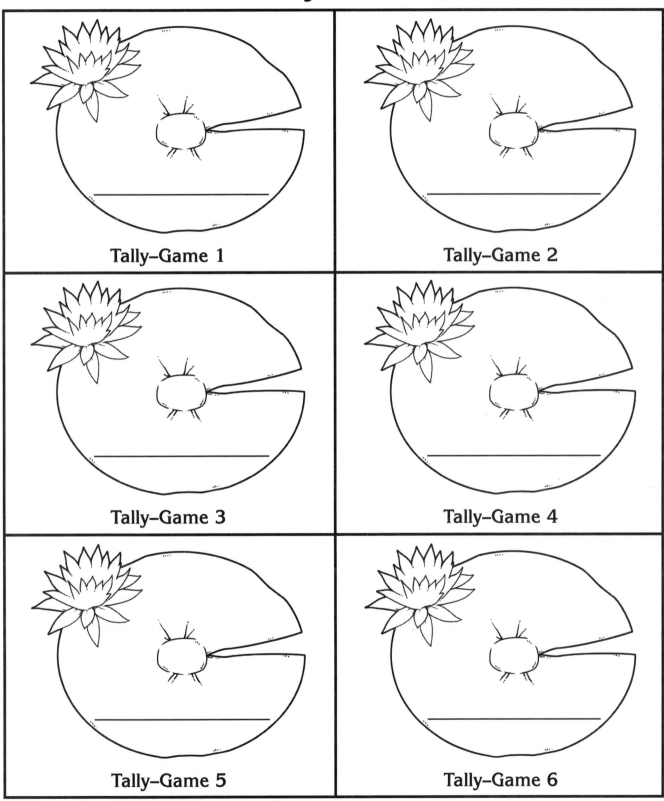

Tally–Game 1

Tally–Game 2

Tally–Game 3

Tally–Game 4

Tally–Game 5

Tally–Game 6

BASIC BEANS

Topic
Place Value

Learning Goals
The students will:
1. trade beans in a base ten system, and
2. construct and solve addition and subtraction problems that involve regrouping.

Guiding Document
*NCTM Standards 2000**
- *Use multiple models to develop initial understandings of place value and the base-ten number system*
- *Develop a sense of whole numbers and represent and use them in flexible ways, including relating, composing, and decomposing numbers*
- *Connect number words and numerals to the quantities they represent, using various physical models and representations*
- *Understand various meanings of addition and subtraction of whole numbers and the relationship between the two operations*

Math
Number operations
    place value

Integrated Processes
Observing
Comparing and contrasting
Relating
Communicating
Applying

Materials
For each group of students:
    set of colored beans (see *Management 1*)
    Base Ten Buckboards (see *Management 2*)
    small zipper-type plastic bags
    Bill of Lading sheet
    Bean Broker Ledgers
    Bean Broker Distribution Records
    one number die
    10 nut cups

For the class:
    transparency of the *Bean Broker Ledgers*
    transparency of the *Bean Broker Distribution Records*
    transparency of the buckboard tree diagram

Background Information
Manipulatives that show a clear relationship between ones, tens, and hundreds are those in which a unit can be used to build ten singles and these are then combined into a single set of ten. The sets of tens can then be collected and combined into sets of one hundred, etc. It is assumed that prior to this lesson students have used such manipulatives. The introduction of *Basic Beans* extends the learners' concept of place value to a more abstract format. Instead of using manipulatives in a one-to-one correspondence, the different colored beans are designated to represent the value of the place. In the case of the beans, ten yellow beans equal one blue bean, and ten blue beans equal one green bean. This concept is a transition to the more traditional base ten place value system.

Management
1. You will need to spray paint lima beans in yellow, green, and blue. Prepare enough beans so that each group has 100 yellow lima beans, 30 blue lima beans, and 10 green lima beans. Place each color in a small zipper-type bag.
2. Copy the *Base Ten Buckboards* on card stock and cut them out for the students to use. Make sure the students know where the *Bean Hopper* is located on each *Base Ten Buckboard*.
3. Have students work in groups of four, if possible. There are enough entries on the *Bean Broker Ledger* for seven groups (28 students). For larger or smaller classrooms, adjust group size.
4. It is strongly recommended that you complete the activity *Hopping on Base* prior to this experience.
5. It is also strongly suggested that you spread this set of experiences over several days so that the students will have time to process and discuss the learning.

Procedure
Part One
1. Distribute the yellow bean bags, nut cups, *Base Ten Buckboards,* and one die to the student groups. Tell them the following scenario:

    Farmer Charlie is taking his beans to market to sell. He can load no more than nine single beans in a bean hopper which means each time he adds the tenth bean he must move them to a basket. Each buckboard can hold ten baskets. Use the die to roll and see how many beans he will be taking to the market.

2. Instruct the students to roll the die ten times and to load the beans at the end of each roll. Remind them of the way Farmer Charlie must load the beans. Beans are to be placed in the bean hopper until the tenth bean is added. Then the ten beans are placed into a basket.

3. Ask the students, "If we added all the groups' beans together, how many total beans can be taken to the market for sale?" Listen for estimations and then ask, "How could we find out the exact number?"

4. If no one suggests it, have the students come to a central place to share the beans and baskets and fill as many buckboards as they can. Have them identify the number of beans they have by the total number of buckboards (hundreds), number of baskets (tens), and the number of single beans (units or ones).

5. Ask the students if they remember the game *Hopping on Base*. Ask, "What did we do in that game that might help us keep track of all the full buckboards and baskets we have?" If no one suggests it, tell them they could use blue beans to represent the baskets and green beans to represent the buckboards.

6. Physically remove one of the full buckboards and place a green bean where it was. Ask, "What does the green bean represent?" [100 yellow beans or 10 full baskets]

7. Replace each full buckboard with a single green bean. Direct the students' attention to the full baskets. Ask them, "What color bean can we use to represent each full basket?" [blue] Replace each full basket with a single blue bean.

8. Point out the green, blue, and yellow beans. Ask the students, "How can we look at these beans and know how many total beans we have for sale?" [Students should be able to tell that the number of green beans represents the number of hundreds, the number of blue beans represents the number of tens, and the yellow beans represent the number of ones they have to sell.]

Part Two
1. Distribute the *Basic Beans Bill of Lading* sheet, number die, nut cups, *Base Ten Buckboards,* and yellow, green, and blue beans bags to each group of four students.

2. Point out the beans that are drawn below the pictures of the bean, basket, and buckboard, and ask the students, "How did we use single beans to represent the ten beans that are in each of the basket and the tens baskets on each

buckboard?" (Lead the students in a discussion on how the yellow beans represented the single beans they were taking to market and that we used a single blue bean to represent each of the baskets and a single green bean to represent a full buckboard. The important transition at this point is that the students understand that the blue bean represents a value of ten since it represents the contents of a basket and the green bean represents a value of 100.)

3. Direct the students' attention to the beans below the buckboard. Place the tree diagram on the overhead. Point out to them that a green bean will be used to represent each buckboard. Ask the students how many baskets the full buckboard can hold. [10] Guide them to understand that the yellow beans represent single beans and each blue bean represents a basket that can hold 10 beans. The green bean would represent 10 baskets. Each basket in turn equals 10 yellow; therefore, 1 green bean equals 100 yellow beans. (If students are still struggling with this concept, you can have them place ten baskets on their buckboard and place ten yellow beans in each basket. They can then manipulate the beans, baskets, and buckboards to aid their understanding.)

4. Direct each group to roll the number die ten times to determine how many beans they will take to the market. Tell the students to fill out their *Bill of Lading* sheets using the different colored beans to represent baskets and single beans.

5. Distribute the *Bean Broker Ledger* sheets. Ask one of the student groups to share the number of beans they are taking to the market. Record their number on the transparency of the *Bean Broker Ledger* you have prepared. Tell each student group to build the number with beans, picture the number in beans, and record the number.

6. Ask a second group to share the number of beans they are taking to market. Illustrate the number on the overhead and direct each group to show the number in all three ways.

7. Direct them to combine the beans and regroup if necessary. Tell them they are to show their work in all three ways. Ask for a student to come to the overhead and share how their group solved the problem. Point out that the total number of beans between the two groups is called *Subtotal #1*.

8. Direct the students to transfer *Subtotal #1* to the top on the second column. Have two more student groups share how many beans they will be taking to market. Let them record each number on the overhead and ask each group to show it in all three ways. Have students add the numbers and regroup when needed. Invite a student to use the overhead to share how his or her group

solved the problem. Point out that this total is called *Subtotal #2*.

9. Tell the students to transfer *Subtotal #2* to the top of the next page. Ask for three different groups to share the number of beans they are taking to the market. Tell each group they must show all three ways to represent each number in the problem.

10. Ask a student to come to the overhead and show how his or her group solved the problem.

Part Three

1. Tell the students one of the other jobs the Bean Broker has is to distribute and sell the beans to the different stores.

2. Hand out the first page of the *Bean Broker Distribution Record* to each group.

3. Tell the students to record the *Beginning Total* at the top of the sheet. Tell them they must use the colored beans to represent the number as well as to color in the picture representation of the number. (You can use the number of beans from the first part of the activity as the number of beans you begin with, but you will need more than 474 beans if you use the numbers listed in the procedures. That is the total number you will be distributing to the three markets. The number selected for distribution can be changed based on the abilities of your students. For example: A total of 500 would give the students subtraction practice that uses regrouping with zeros in the ones and tens places, or you could select numbers that would not require the students to regroup.)

4. Guide the students through the first distribution. Tell them that the Bean Broker needs to distribute two buckboards and three baskets to Mr. Mole's Market. Tell them they must show you this in beans both real and representational as well as in numbers. Remind them the 230 beans, two buckboards and three baskets, must come from the beginning total. The remaining beans would be *Subtotal #1*.

5. Direct the students to record *Subtotal #1* at the bottom.

6. Have them transfer *Subtotal #1* to the top of the second column for the second delivery. Tell them that one buckboard and six baskets needs to be delivered to Miss Vole's Vegetable Stand. Tell the students they must show this delivery in the same way they did for the first. Monitor the groups to check to see if they are recording the transaction correctly.

7. Hand out a copy of the second *Bean Broker Distribution Record* to each student. Guide the students through the final transaction by telling them that the final delivery is to Mrs. Gerbil's General Store and she needs eight baskets and

four beans. Ask the students to show this final transaction in only pictures and numbers. Try to let them figure out that they must transfer *Subtotal #2* from the first student page to the second student page. Guide them only if they are having difficulty with this part of the process. Monitor students as they are working through this final step.

8. Discuss with the students how the pictures represented the numbers and helped them to solve the problem without needing the real beans.

9. Ask the students to solve the word problem on the final page.

Connecting Learning

1. Why do you think you would want a single blue bean to represent 10 beans? [It is easier to count sets than singles.]

2. How was the activity *Basic Beans* like adding and subtracting?

3. If the Bean Brokers have four full buckboards and six baskets, how many total beans do they have? How do you know? What would that number look like in beans? [460, 4 green beans and 6 blue beans]

4. What does each different color bean represent? [Different values: the yellows are ones, the blues are tens, and the greens are hundreds.]

5. In this activity, what do the beans represent? [numbers]

6. When you use numbers in addition and subtraction, what do the numbers represent? [The numbers represent real things.]

Evidence of Learning

1. Listen for student talk as they place the beans in the hopper, the beans in the baskets, and the baskets on the buckboards. They should be able to explain the relationship between the beans, baskets, and buckboards. The yellow beans represent ones, baskets represent tens, and buckboards represent hundreds. They need to be able to communicate that the blue beans can represent the baskets (10s) and the green beans can represent the buckboards (100s).

2. Check for correct recording on student record sheets. Look for correct picture records as well as number records. Student work should reflect an understanding that yellow beans represent ones, blue beans represent tens, and green beans represent hundreds. The modeling of addition and subtraction should also show that they understand part-part-whole relationships.

BASIC BEANS

The Bean Broker's Office buys beans from many farmers. They need to keep track of how many full buckboards they have as well as full baskets and single beans. Each full buckboard would have 10 baskets of beans. Each basket would have 10 beans in it. They use one green bean to represent a full buckboard.

1 green bean = 10 blue beans = 100 yellow beans

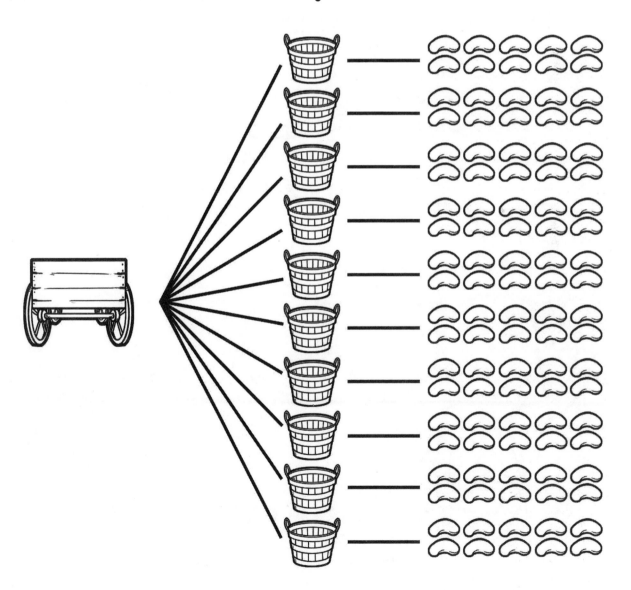

BASIC BEANS

Bean Hopper

Base Ten Buckboards

Bean Hopper

Base Ten Buckboards

BASIC BEANS
Bill of Lading

Farmers _____, _____, _____, _____,

Our group had _____ beans to take to the market to sell.

That means we had _____ baskets and _____ single beans.

Record in Numbers _____ _____ _____

| Number of Buckboards | Number of Baskets | Number of Beans |

Picture Record

Green   Blue   Yellow

We can use _____ blue beans to represent the _____ baskets we had.

At the Bean Broker's Office we will show _____ blue beans and _____ yellow beans. They will know that this is _____ beans we have for sale.

BASIC BEANS

Bean Broker Ledger

Buckboards Green	Baskets Blue	Beans Yellow

Group 1
Picture
Record

Group 2
Picture
Record

+

Subtotal #1
Picture
Record

Buckboards Green	Baskets Blue	Beans Yellow

Subtotal #1
Picture
Record

Group 3
Picture
Record

Group 4
Picture
Record

+

Subtotal #2
Picture
Record

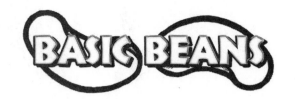

BASIC BEANS

Bean Broker Ledger

Buckboards	Baskets	Beans
Green	Blue	Yellow

Subtotal #2

Picture Record

Group 5

Picture Record

Group 6

Picture Record

Group 7

Picture Record

+

Subtotal #3

Picture Record

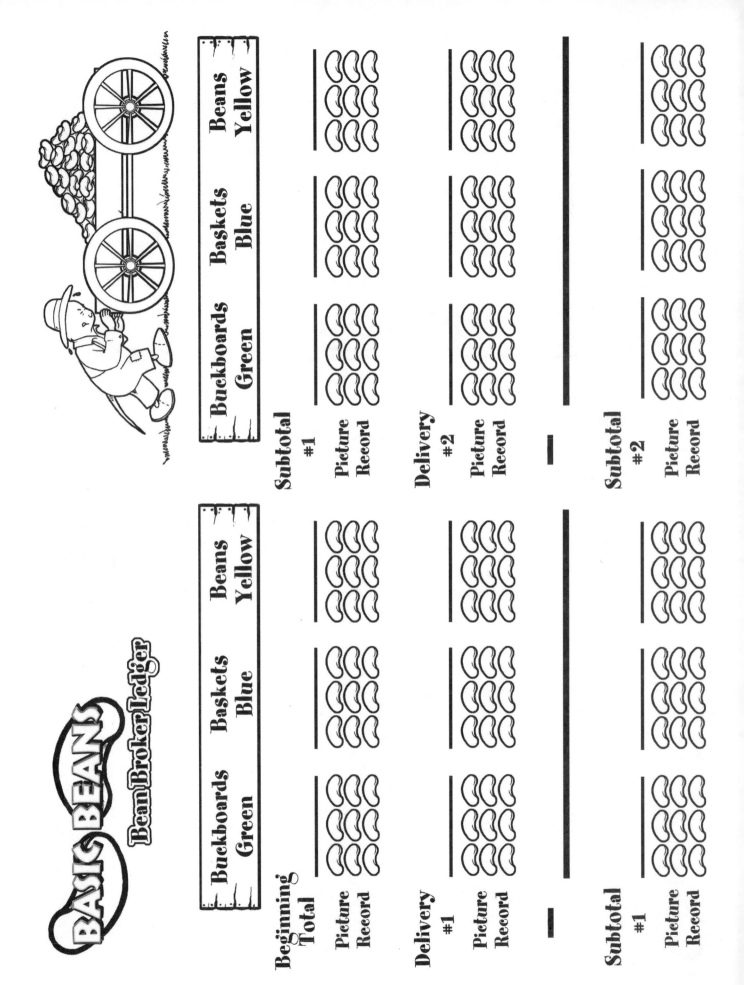

BASIC BEANS
Bean Broker Ledger

Buckboards Green	Baskets Blue	Beans Yellow

Beginning Total

Picture Record

Delivery #1

Picture Record

Subtotal #1

Picture Record

Buckboards Green	Baskets Blue	Beans Yellow

Subtotal #1

Picture Record

Delivery #2

Picture Record

Subtotal #2

Picture Record

The Bean Brokers need to make another delivery to Mr. Frog's Toadside Stand. They have 356 beans before the delivery and Mr. Frog needs 179 beans. How many beans will the Bean Brokers have left after the delivery? Show your work in numbers and pictures.

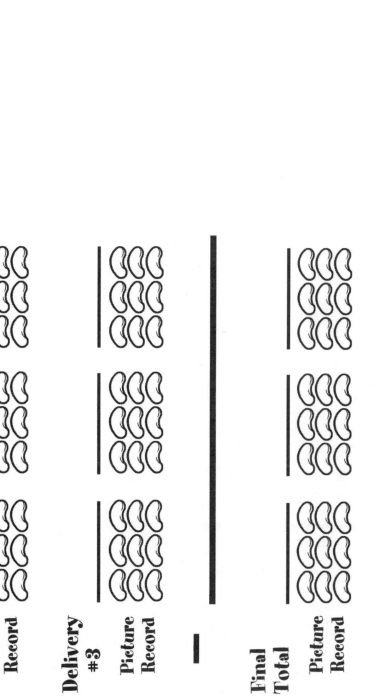

BASIC BEANS

Bean Broker Distribution Record

Buckboards Green	Baskets Blue	Beans Yellow
Subtotal #2		
Picture Record		
Delivery #3		
Picture Record		
Final Total		
Picture Record		

Money Has Its Place

Topic
Operations

Learning Goal
The students will construct manipulative models to represent operations of addition and subtraction of money using one-, two-, and three-digit numbers.

Guiding Document
NCTM Standards 2000*
- *Use a variety of methods and tools to compute, including objects, mental computation, estimation, paper and pencil, and calculators*
- *Understand various meanings of addition and subtraction of whole numbers and the relationship between the two operations*
- *Understand the effects of adding and subtracting whole numbers*
- *Develop a sense of whole numbers and represent and use them in flexible ways, including relating, composing, and decomposing numbers*
- *Connect number words and numerals to the quantities they represent, using various physical models and representations*

Math
Operations
  addition and subtraction

Integrated Processes
Observing
Recording
Comparing and contrasting
Communicating
Applying

Materials
For each student:
  Operation Boards
  money (see *Management 1*)
  Place Value Labels

Background Information
Building models of numbers and depicting operations using manipulatives help learners build an understanding of the complicated procedures of grouping and regrouping used in operations. This lesson takes the students through a step by step process in which they build models, move objects, and find solutions to addition and subtraction problems.

Money is used in this experience for its real-world application. This activity uses pennies, dimes, and dollars. This relates to the ones, tens, and hundreds used in other place value experiences. The grouping of 10 pennies into a set that can be traded for a dime helps build the understanding for the need for regrouping. Placing these coins on an *Operation Board* labeled in ones, tens, and hundreds continues to build a knowledge base of place value. Using the manipulatives on an *Operation Board*, combined with recording, helps the students begin to build a relationship between the numbers and the placement of these numbers related to place value.

Management
1. Copy enough coins and bills for each student based on the equations being taught at the time.
2. Have the students use the grid to record the addition and subtraction problems with money.

	3	.	8	9	
+	1	.	0	7	
	4	.	9	6	

Procedure
Part One—Addition with Money
1. Give the students yellow, blue, and green *Operation Boards, Place Value Labels,* and coins and dollar bills. Direct them to position the boards with the pink section at the bottom. Ask them to place *ones, tens, and hundreds* labels above the appropriate boards. Direct them to place one penny beside the ones label, one dime beside the tens label, and one dollar beside the hundreds label.
2. Give the students a problem to solve such as: Betty had 1 dollar and 3 dimes. She found 3 dimes and 6 pennies. How much money does she now have?
3. Direct the students to place the money in the correct sections on the *Operation Boards.* Tell them to combine the sections and move the coins to the pink section of their *Operation Boards.* Have them record the actions on the answer grid sheet.

4. Direct the students to work this problem on their *Operation Boards:* Juan had three dollars and 75 cents. He earned five dollars and 55 cents. How much can he now deposit into his savings account?

5. Ask the students what they needed to do in this problem that was different than the first problem. [This problem requires regrouping both in the ones place and the tens place.]

6. Work additional problems involving the addition of money with and without regrouping.

Part Two—Subtraction with Money

1. Give the students yellow, blue, and green *Operation Boards, Place Value Labels,* and coins and dollar bills. Direct them to position the boards with the pink section at the top. Ask them to place *ones, tens,* and *hundreds* labels above the appropriate boards. Direct them to place one penny beside the ones label, one dime beside the tens label, and one dollar beside the hundreds label.

2. Give the students the following problem to solve. Lakeshia had seven dollars and 39 cents. She bought a magazine that cost two dollars and 25 cents. How much does she have left?

3. Have the students place the seven dollars and 39 cents in the pink section. Ask them to move two dollars and 25 cents into the middle section. Tell students to move the remaining money into the bottom section. Record the actions on the answer grid sheet.

4. Present the students with the following problem: Nick has six dollars. He spends four dollars and 86 cents at the school store, how much does he have left?

5. Tell the students to place six dollars in the top pink section of their *Operation Boards.* Inform them that they will need to subtract four dollars and 86 cents from the six dollars. Point out that in subtraction and addition we begin in the ones place. Ask them how we can take six away from nothing. If no one suggests it, point out that they trade one of the dollars for ten dimes and one of the dimes for ten pennies. Guide them in the recording of this process on the answer grid.

6. Work additional problems involving subtracting of money with and without regrouping.

Connecting Learning

1. How are pennies, dimes, and dollars related to place value?

2. What do you need to do when you have more than nine pennies in the ones place or nine dimes in the tens place?

3. Why is it important to look for + and − symbols before trying to work a problem?

4. When you have a four in the hundreds place, zero in the tens place, and you need to subtract three tens from it, what do you need to do?

5. Build a number story using money on your board and then write the number story using numerals. Share your story with someone and have him or her solve the problem

Evidence of Learning

1. Look for appropriate placement of manipulatives on the *Operation Boards* to match target numbers.

2. Look for correct recording and solving of problems on the answer grid.

3. Listen for understanding as students explain the need for and process of regrouping.

* Reprinted with permission from *Principles and Standards for School Mathematics,* 2000 by the National Council of Teachers of Mathematics. All rights reserved.

Money Has Its Place

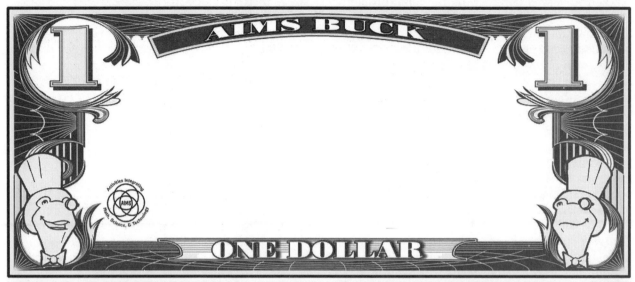

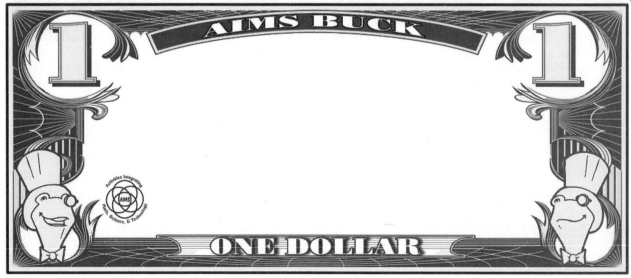

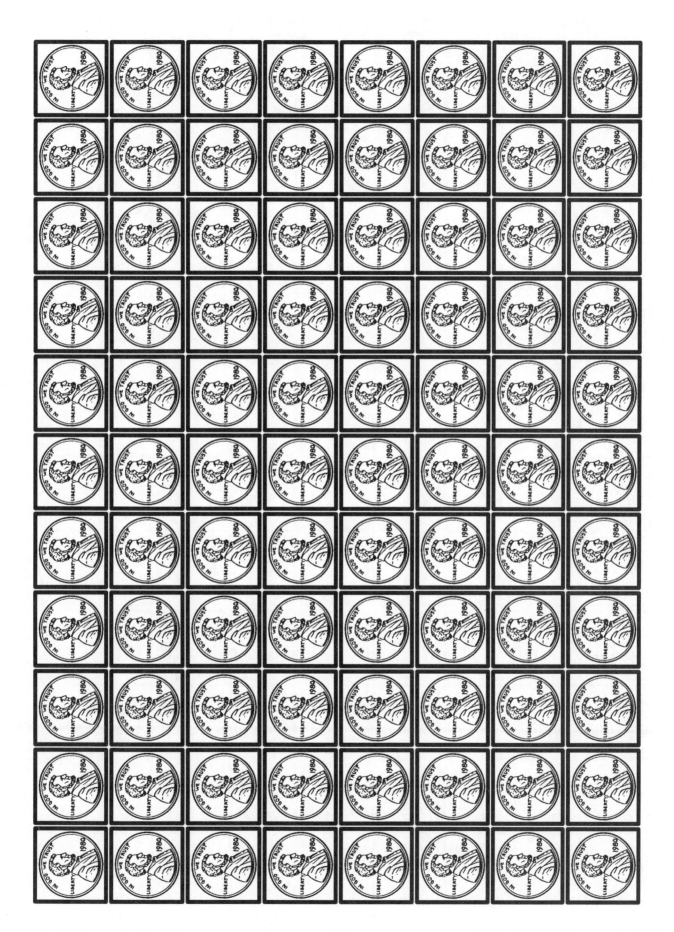

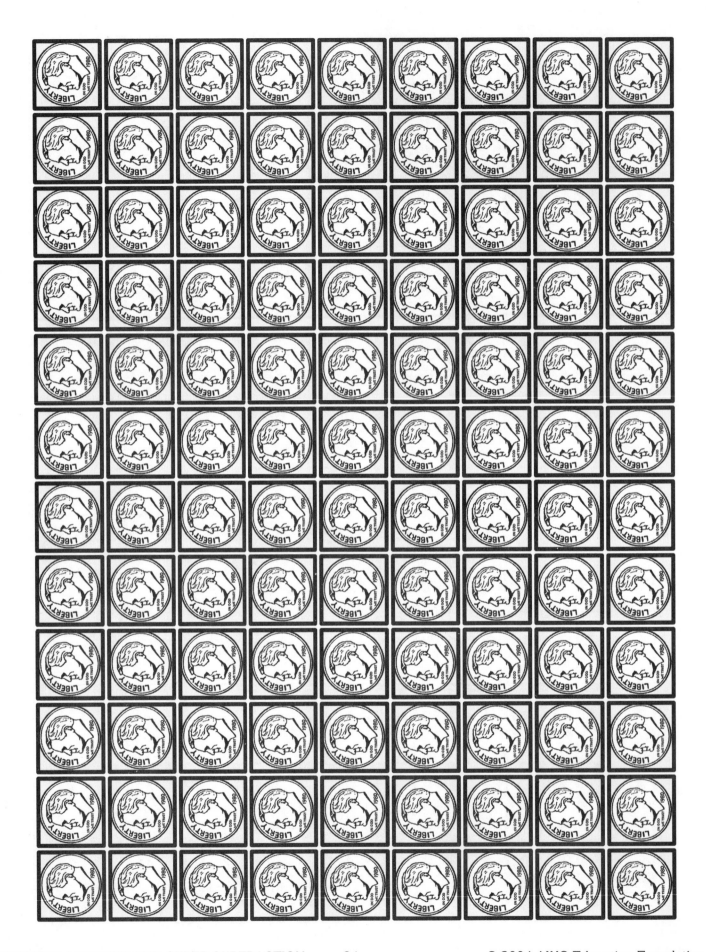

Meaningful Problem Solving

Big Ideas in Problem Solving

- Patterns are key
- Process oriented
- Multiple methods
- Persistence must be developed
- Divergent thinking is important

Meaningful Problem Solving

Key Skills in Problem Solving

- Communicating mathematically
- Thinking divergently
- Looking for multiple methods
- Asking insightful questions (What if ...?)
- Looking for multiple solutions
- Doing similar simpler problems
- Making charts and tables
- Drawing diagrams and pictures
- Working backwards

Topics
Problem Solving, Addition

Key Questions
1. How can you determine what numbers belong in the squares based on the number of manipulatives in the hexagon, triangle, and circle?
2. How can you determine the number of manipulatives that belong in the triangle, hexagon, and circle based on the numbers in the squares?

Learning Goals
The students will:
1. create an addition problem using the *Shape Frame Math* mat,
2. use problem-solving skills to solve for missing addends on their classmates' mats, and
3. look for patterns in their mats and in the mats of their classmates.

Guiding Document
NCTM Standards 2000*
- *Count with understanding and recognize "how many" in sets of objects*
- *Connect number words and numerals to the quantities they represent, using various physical models and representations*
- *Develop and use strategies for whole-number computations, with a focus on addition and subtraction*

Math
Number and operations
    addition
    odd and even
Problem solving
Patterns

Integrated Processes
Observing
Collecting and recording data
Interpreting data
Comparing and contrasting

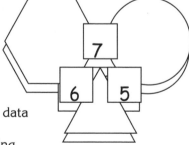

Materials
For each student:
    Shape Frame Math mat
    Shape Frame Math solutions page
    10 or more small manipulatives (see *Management 1*)

Management
1. Students will need at least 10 manipulatives to put in the spaces on the *Shape Frame Math* mat. These manipulatives should be small enough to fit in the spaces and be easily counted. Items such as beans, buttons, or math chips all work well.
2. If you are working with young learners, give them only 10 manipulatives. Increase the number of manipulatives according to the addition skills of your students.
3. You may want to laminate the mat so that students can write the sums in the squares using dry erase pens rather than having to erase their answers for each new problem. Another option is to give students small sticky notes on which to write the sums so that they can be removed for each new problem.
4. This game format is designed to practice addition at the problem-solving level. Use it multiple times throughout the year for extended practice.

Procedure
Part One
1. Give each student a *Shape Frame Math* mat and some manipulatives.
2. Direct them to place a different number of manipulatives in each large shape: hexagon, circle, and triangle.
3. Tell the students to add the number of manipulatives in the hexagon to the number of manipulatives in the triangle and to record this sum in the square that overlaps both these shapes.
4. Direct the students to do the same with the other shapes, recording the sums in the overlapping squares.
5. Tell them to remove the manipulatives, leaving only the recorded sums in the squares.
6. Have students trade their mats with other classmates. Challenge them to determine the missing manipulatives, or addends, based on the recorded answers. If their numbers add up correctly, they will have solved the problem.
7. Continue this process, having students exchange mats with different classmates.
8. Challenge the students to mentally solve for the missing addends.

Part Two
1. Continue the learning game as described in *Part One*, adding the element of keeping a record of each solution. Give each student a *Shape Frame Math* solutions page.
2. Direct the students to record their challenge problems and solutions on the *Shape Frame Math* solutions pages.
3. Discuss any patterns or similarities they notice among the problems and solutions.

Connecting Learning
1. What method(s) did you use to solve the problems?
2. How does this compare to your classmates' methods? Are they the same or different?
3. Were some problems easier to solve? ...harder to solve? Why?
4. What did you do to solve the problems when the manipulatives were not available?
5. Look at the combination of addends used in the three large shapes on each of the problems. Describe what you see. Do you find any that are all even? ...all odd?
6. Do you think you could design a challenge problem that would work in this format that would include all even addends? [yes] ...all odd addends? [yes] Explain why. (As long as the students can control the total number of manipulatives that they place in the shapes, they will always be able to make the addends either all odd or all even. If the total number of manipulatives is fixed, then the addends cannot be all even or all odd.)

7. Look at the combination of numbers used in the three squares on each of the problems on the *Shape Frame Math* solutions pages. Do you find any that are all even? ...all odd? Describe what you discover.
8. Do you think you could design a challenge problem that would work in this format that would have three even sums? [yes] ...three odd sums? [no] Explain why. [When all of the addends are even, the result is three even sums. When all of the addends are odd, the result is three even sums. When the addends are both odd and even, the result is two odd sums and one even sum.]

Evidence of Learning
1. Check for accuracy when adding and recording totals.
2. Listen for insight in problem-solving techniques as students discuss patterns discovered.

Extensions
1. Older students can be challenged to explore the nature of odd and even numbers. What happens when you add two odd numbers? ...two even numbers? ...an odd and an even number? How does this relate to the problems you were able to create with the mat?
2. Create a mat that has four shapes and repeat the activity. How do these results compare with those from a three-shape mat?

*   Reprinted with permission from *Principles and Standards for School Mathematics*, 2000 by National Council of Teachers of Mathematics. All rights reserved.

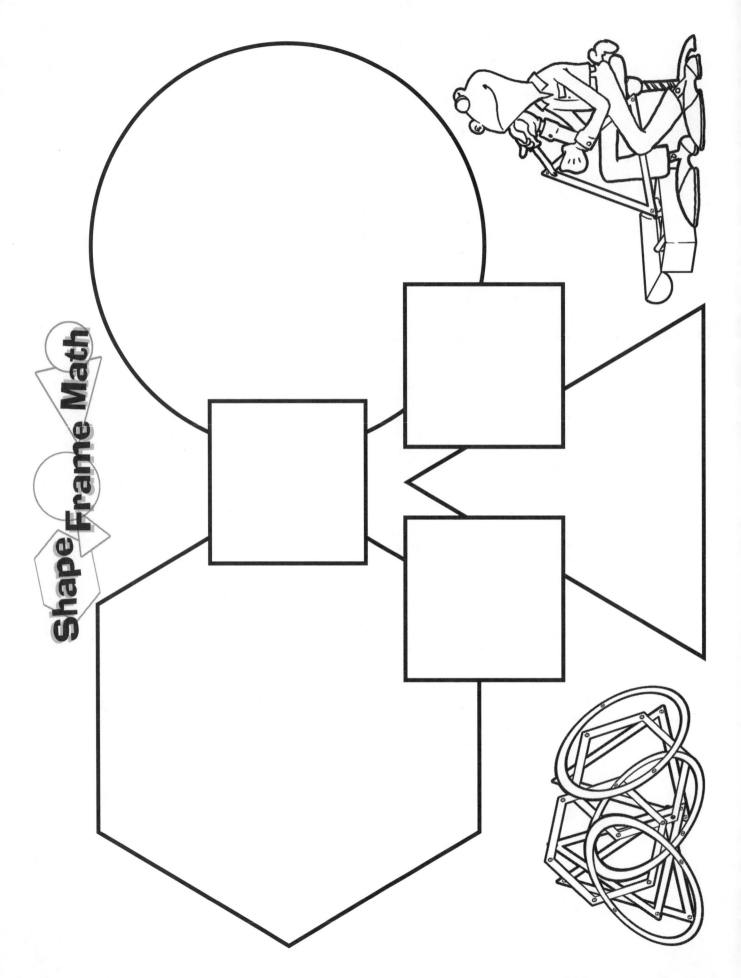

Shape Frame Math

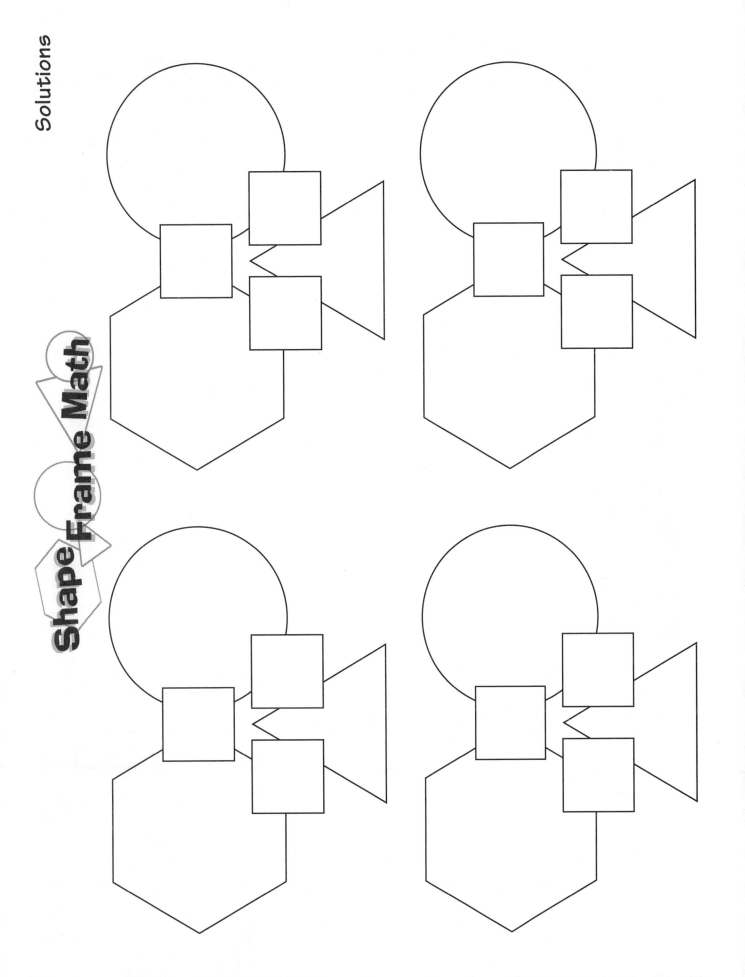

Shape Frame Math

Making Arrangements

Topic
Place value

Learning Goals
Students will:
1. recognize that groupings of one, tens, and hundreds can be taken apart in several ways; and
2. realize there are patterns in the ways that numbers are formed.

Guiding Document
NCTM Standards 2000*

- *Understand numbers, ways of representing numbers, relationships among numbers and number systems*
- ** Understand the place-value structure of the base-ten numbers system and be able to represent and compare whole numbers and decimals*
- *Recognize equivalent representations for the same number and generate them by decomposing and composing numbers*

Background Information
Children often are able to state the proper number of ones, tens, and hundreds, but find it difficult to break a multi-digit number into different arrangements. This activity challenges students to realize that the groupings of ones, tens, and hundreds can be taken apart in several ways.

Materials
For each group of students:
   one arrangements recording chart
   Base Ten Blocks
   pencils

For the teacher:
   transparency of arrangements recording chart

Procedure
1. Distribute recording chart and Base Ten Blocks to pairs or trios of students.
2. Ask a student to build the number 148 with the Base Ten Blocks.
3. Have several students share other possible arrangements.
4. In small groups of two and three, have students build the number and record their arrangements on the student page until they find *all* possible arrangements.
5. As they are building and recording, encourage groups to share observations and try to discover patterns in their arrangements.

Connecting Learning
1. How many different arrangements are there? [20] How do you know if you have all the possible

solutions? [There are various patterns to the different arrangements.]
2. What are some of the patterns found in the chart? [There are consecutive counting numbers in the tens place (0–4 are used twice). There are possible block totals from 13–148. There are differences of nine blocks used in each total.]
3. What do you suppose would happen to the total number of arrangements if the digit in the ones place were raised or lowered? ...the digit in the tens or the hundreds?

Evidence of Learning
1. Look for the correct number of solutions and adequate expression of finding all of the possible arrangements.
2. Question individual students or groups while they are working. Do you need Base Ten Blocks to manipulate while finding all the possible arrangements? Listen as they explain the patterns that help them solve the problem.
3. Assign a different number or have students choose their own number to find all the possible arrangements.

Solutions
Number 148

Groups of Hundreds	Groups of Tens	Groups of Ones	Total # of Blocks
1	0	48	49
1	1	38	40
1	2	28	31
1	3	18	22
1	4	8	13
0	0	148	148
0	1	138	139
0	2	128	130
0	3	118	121
0	4	108	112
0	5	98	103
0	6	88	94
0	7	78	85
0	8	68	76
0	9	58	67
0	10	48	58
0	11	38	49
0	12	28	40
0	13	18	31
0	14	8	22

* Reprinted with permission from *Principles and Standards for School Mathematics,* 2000 by the National Council of Teachers of Mathematics. All rights reserved.

Making Arrangements

NUMBER _____

GROUPS OF HUNDREDS	GROUPS OF TENS	GROUPS OF ONES	TOTAL NUMBER OF GROUPS

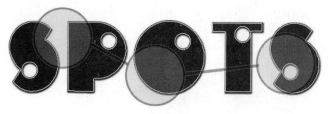

Topic
Problem Solving, Addition

Key Question
How can you arrange numbers in a variety of arrays so that each line equals a specific target sum?

Learning Goals
The students will:
1. use problem-solving skills to arrange numbers so that they total a target sum,
2. gain practice using addition to solve problems, and
3. look for patterns in their solutions.

Guiding Document
NCTM Standards 2000*
- *Develop fluency with basic number combinations for addition and subtraction*
- *Understand the effects of adding and subtracting whole numbers*
- *Develop and use strategies for whole-number computations, with a focus on addition and subtraction*

Math
Number and operations
    addition
Patterns
Problem solving

Integrated Processes
Observing
Comparing and contrasting
Collecting and recording data
Interpreting data

Materials
For each student:
    Math Spots mats
    Math Spots recording pages
    number cards (see *Management 2*)

Management
1. This game format is designed to practice addition at the problem-solving level. Use it multiple times throughout the year for extended practice.
2. Students will need number cards labeled with the numerals one to six. These cards should fit into the spaces on the student sheets. Scratch paper

cut into small squares, math chips, punch-out circles, and area tiles all work well.
3. There are several different *Math Spots* mats which vary in difficulty based on their configuration and number of spaces. Choose the mat(s) which are most appropriate for your students and use those.

Procedure
1. Give each student one of the *Math Spots* mats and a set of number cards.
2. Direct the students to write the appropriate target sum (in pencil) on the line below the array. The possible target sums for the first array are:

8, 9, 10

3. Challenge the students to arrange their number cards in the spaces so that the sum of each line in the array equals one of the target sums.
4. Once students find a solution, direct them to record it on the appropriate *Math Spots* recording page.
5. Challenge the students to find as many different solutions for this target sum as they can. Have them record their solutions and compare them with other classmates.
6. Assign a second target sum for the array. Have students find as many solutions as they can for this new sum.
7. Continue by assigning any remaining target sums.
8. Repeat this process with as many of the different arrays as time allows. This time, however, let students determine the target sums.
9. Close with a time of class discussion in which students look for patterns in their solutions and describe what they find.

Connecting Learning
1. What did you do that helped you solve the problems?
2. How does your strategy compare to the strategies used by your classmates?
3. Were some problems easier to solve? ...harder to solve? Why?
4. Do any numbers work as target sums? [no] Why

or why not? [There are only a few possible sums, depending on the arrangement. Different target sums require different numbers to be placed in the arrays.]

5. Does it matter whether or not a target sum is odd or even? [It depends on the array.] How do you know this?
6. Do you think the class has discovered all the possible solutions for each target sum for the different arrays? How can you find out?
7. Look at the solutions on your recording pages. What patterns do you see?

Triangular Array
1. Look at all of the corner numbers. What do you notice?
2. Look at all of the inside numbers. What do you notice?
3. Is nine the smallest sum possible using the numbers one to six? [yes] Why? [Since six is the largest number, the lowest sum possible is $6 + 1 + 2 = 9$.]
4. Is 12 the largest sum possible using the numbers one to six? [yes] Why? [Since one is the smallest number, the highest sum possible is $1 + 5 + 6 = 12$.]

Evidence of Learning
1. Check solutions for accuracy.
2. Listen for logical explanations for number placement in the arrays.

Extensions
Use different numbers in the arrays to reach different target sums and compare the solutions for patterns.

Cross Array
1. Use the numbers 2–6 to get target sums of 11 and 13.
2. Use the first five odd numbers to get target sums of 13 and 15.
3. Use the first five even numbers to get target sums of 16 and 18.

Zigzag Array
1. Use the numbers 2–6 to get a target sum of 9.
2. Use the first five even numbers to get target sums of 12 and 14. Is it possible to use the first five odd numbers in this array? Why or why not?

U-shaped Array
1. Use the numbers 2–6 to get a target sum of 9. Why is there only one target sum when the numbers 2–6 are used?
2. Use the first five even numbers to get target sums of 12 and 14. Is it possible to use the first five odd numbers in this array? Why or why not?

Triangular Array
1. Use the numbers 2–7 to get target sums of 12, 13, 14, and 15.
2. Use the first six odd numbers to get target sums of 15, 17, 19, and 21.
3. Use the first six even numbers to get target sums of 18, 20, 22, and 24.

* Reprinted with permission from *Principles and Standards for School Mathematics*, 2000 by National Council of Teachers of Mathematics. All rights reserved.

MATH SPOTS

Arrange the numbers 1, 2, 3, 4, and 5 in the circles so that each line has the same sum.

Target Sum

MATH SPOTS

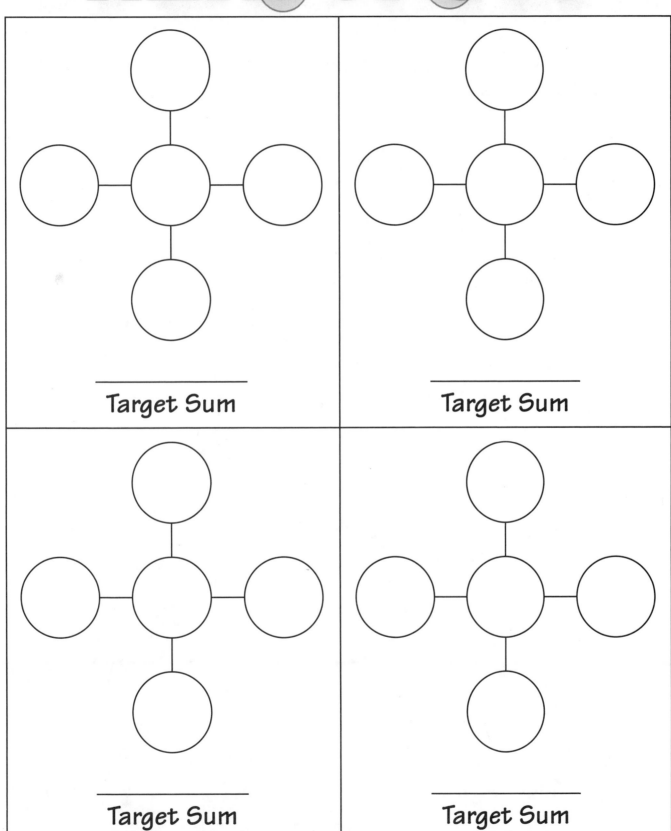

Target Sum

Target Sum

Target Sum

Target Sum

Arrange the numbers 1, 2, 3, 4, and 5 in the circles so that each line has the same sum.

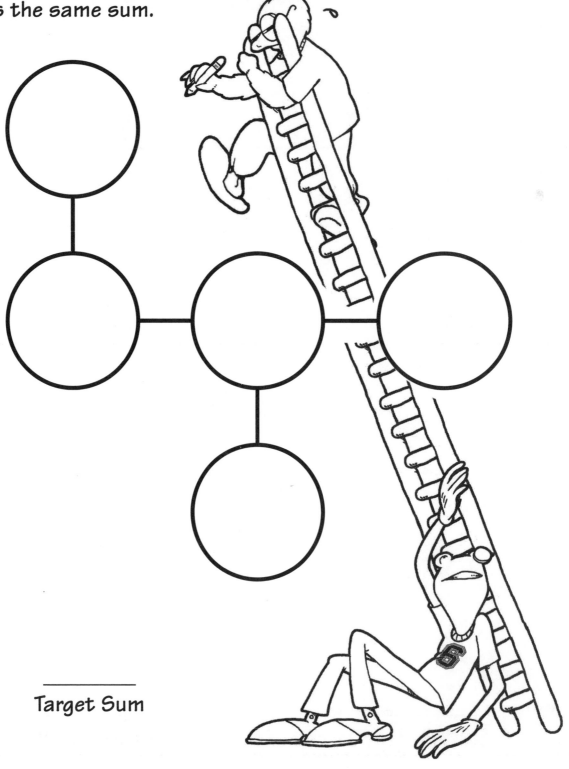

_____
Target Sum

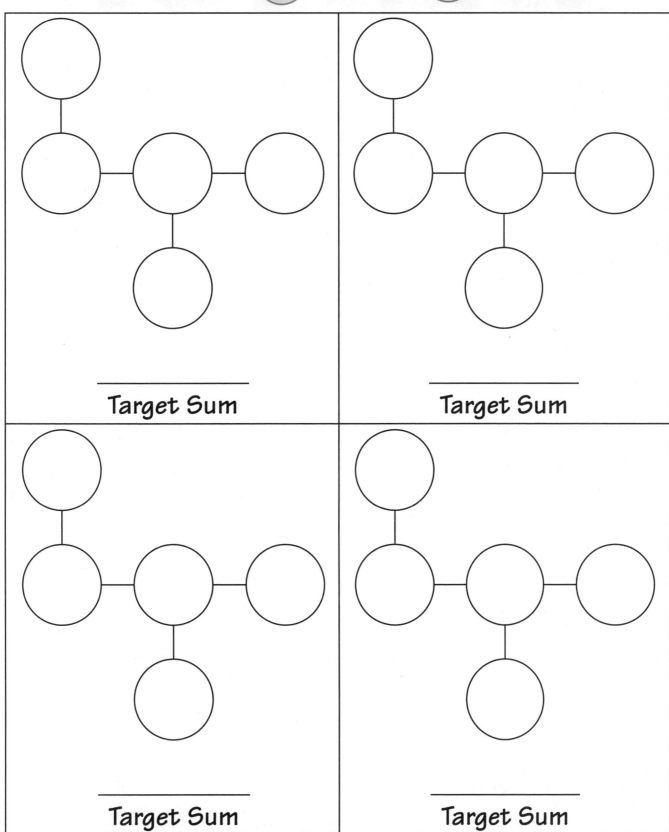

Target Sum

Target Sum

Target Sum

Target Sum

MATH SPOTS

Arrange the numbers 1, 2, 3, 4 and 5 in the circles so that each line has the same sum.

Target Sum

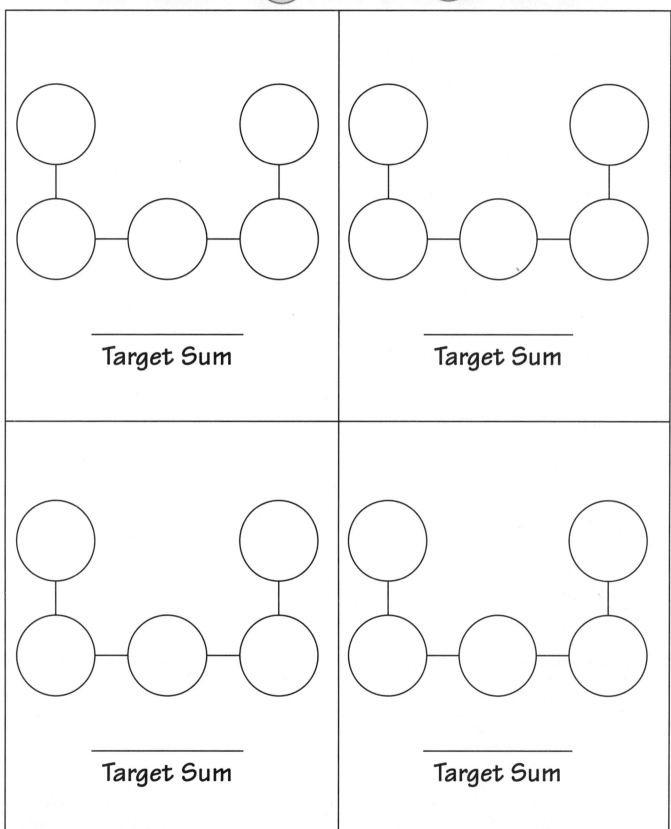

Target Sum

Target Sum

Target Sum

Target Sum

MATH SPOTS

Please use the numbers 1-7. Find a solution
in which the sum is the same along each of the lines.

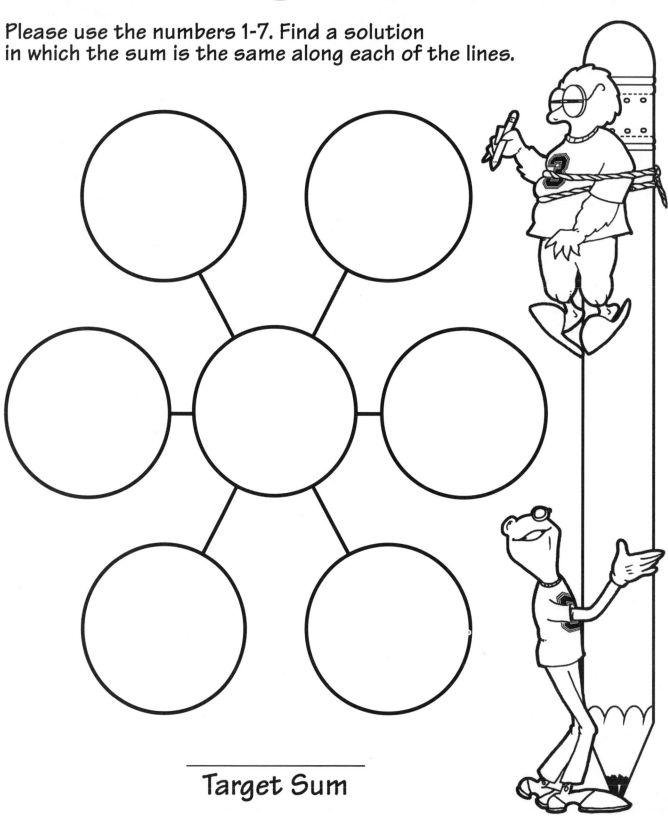

Target Sum

MATH SPOTS

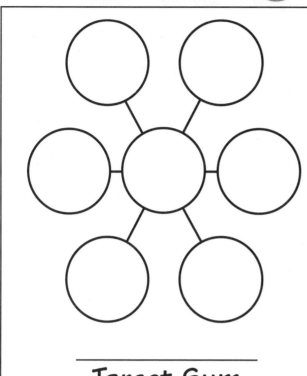

Target Sum

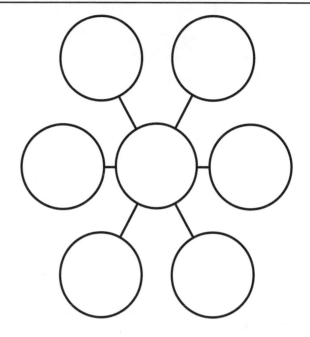

Target Sum

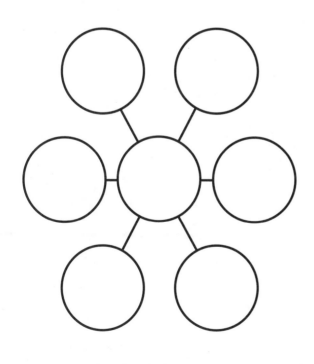

Target Sum

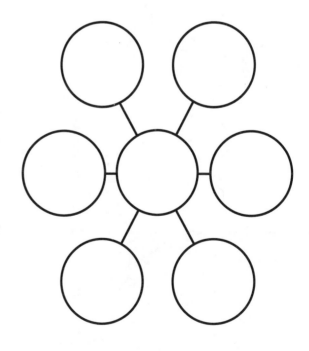

Target Sum

Please use the numbers 1-9. Find a solution in which the sum is the same along each of the lines.

Target Sum

MATH SPOTS

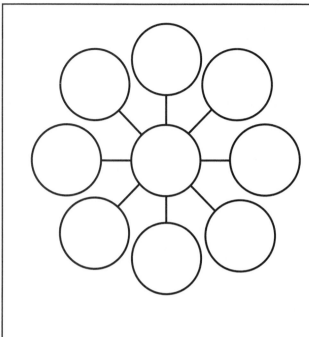

Target Sum

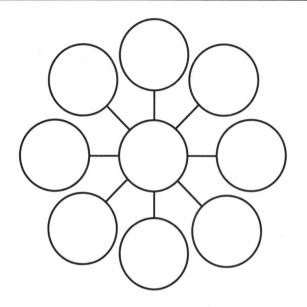

Target Sum

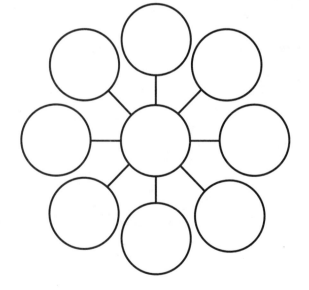

Target Sum

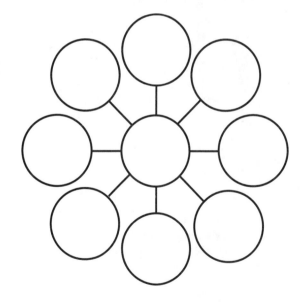

Target Sum

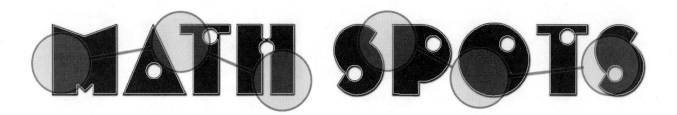

MATH SPOTS

Please use the numbers 1-9. Arrange them so the sum is correct for the two addends.

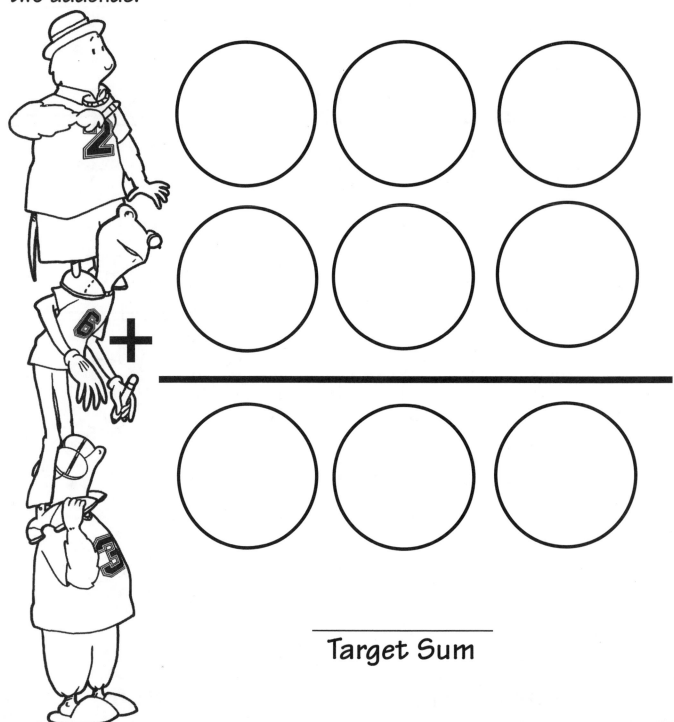

Target Sum

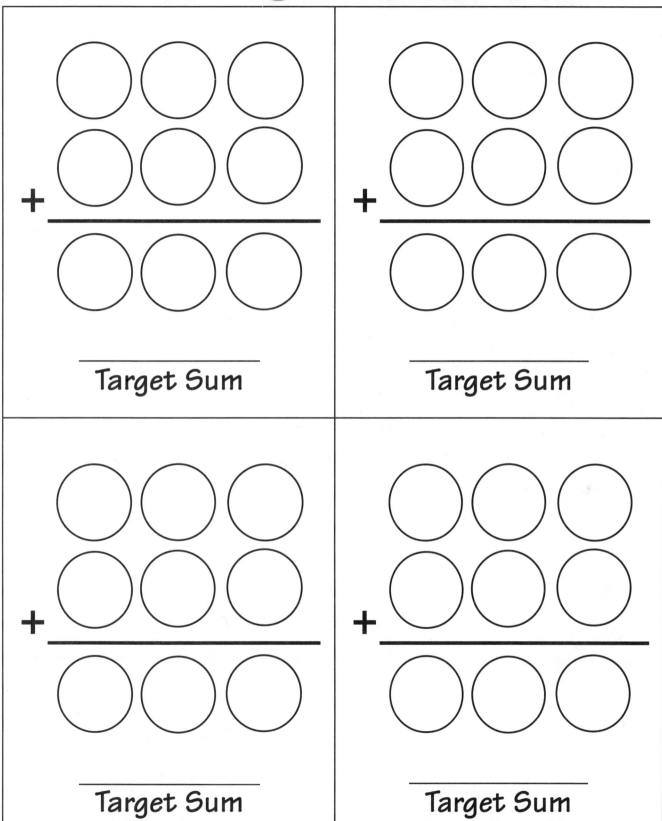

+

Target Sum

+

Target Sum

+

Target Sum

+

Target Sum

Arrange the numbers 1, 2, 3, 4, 5 and 6 in the circles so that each line has the same sum.

——————
Target Sum

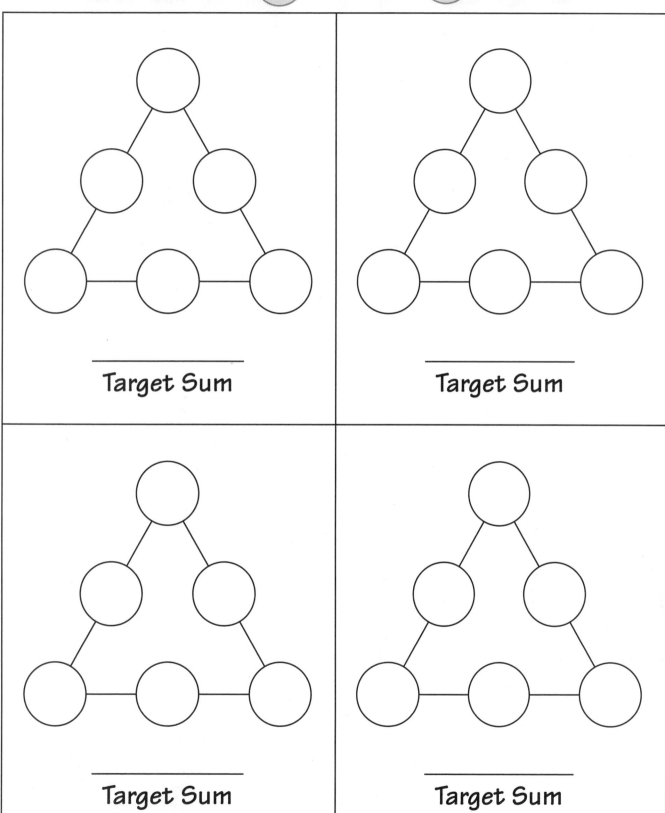

Target Sum

Target Sum

Target Sum

Target Sum

DIVING into DIFFIES

Directions

Choose four numbers, 1 through 9. Write them in a row. Find the difference between each pair and then the two end numbers and record in a row just beneath the first row of numbers. Repeat the process until you get to a row of zeros.

Example

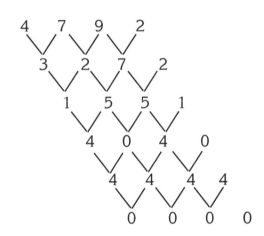

This is an example of a six-level diffie. There are six rows of differences to get to a row of zeros. Each row is a sequence of differences from the row above.

Challenge

Design a diffie of your own. How many levels were you able to get? What numbers need to be side by side to get the highest level diffie? What patterns do you notice? What happens if you include zero? What does the largest diffie that could be designed look like? What would happen if I put five numbers in a row? Could I do this with numbers with double digits? Do a "diffie" and post it on the board. Look for patterns.

DIVING into DIFFIES

Diamond Diffies

Diamond Diffies offer an opportunity for students to use their knowledge of the basic subtraction facts in a playful, intelligent way. To play the game, one starts by writing a number in each of the four circles in the corners of the array. Two corner numbers are then considered at a time and their difference is recorded in the circle between them. For example, with starting numbers of 17, 12, 7, and 3, we would have the illustrated situation shown on the right.

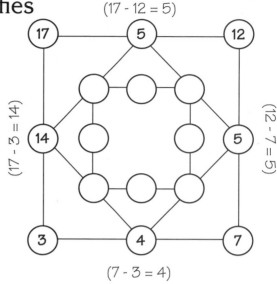

The process of "differencing" continues. Now the previous "differences" are considered in pairs. The difference of each pair is again recorded in the circle between them. Our example continues on the left.

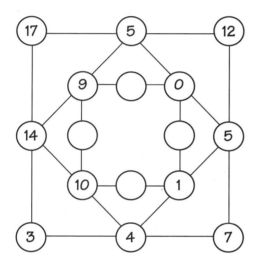

The "differencing" is done once again, and the final result is:

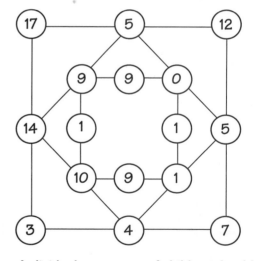

After working a few of these problems, some questions might arise. Individuals or groups of children should investigate these, and records of results should be kept.

Reflecting on Learning
1. If you kept "differencing" long enough, would all arrays eventually end up with four zeros?
2. Is there any way to predict how many "differencings" must be done before the four "differences" are all zeros?
3. What do you think would happen if you tried a triangular diffy?

DIVING into DIFFIES

Start with a number in each corner and work toward the center.

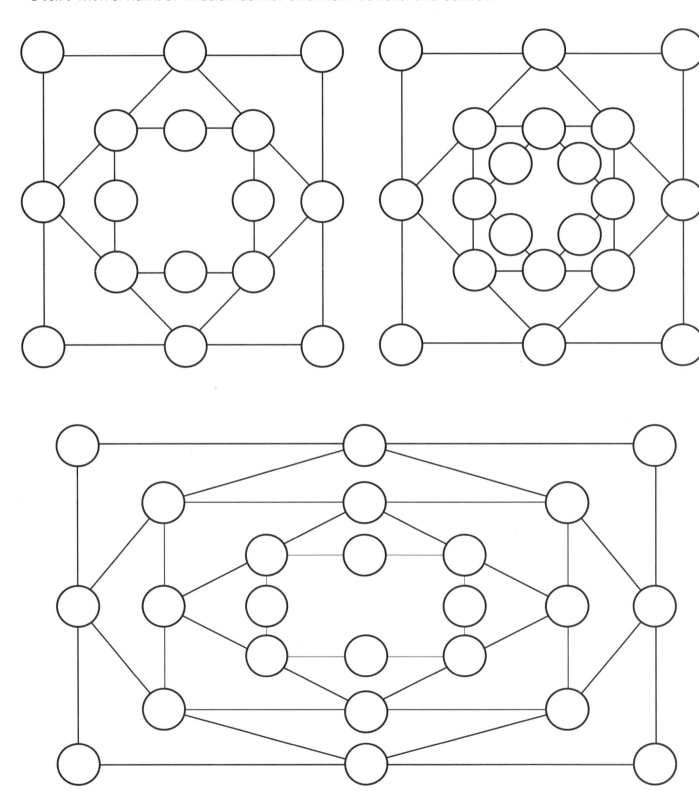

TRIANGULAR DIFFY

Digits in *Disguise*

This activity has students creating their own number riddles and provides an excellent opportunity for students to think and communicate mathematically.

Digits in Disguise is an adaptation of a language arts activity called "Who am I?" This activity, from Bob and Marlene McCracken (consultants in reading and writing), was intended to help students become better at using descriptive language in their writing. In the first part of the activity, students picked a character from a book they were reading and then listed as many adjectives and/or phrases as they could describing that character. In the second part, students used this list to come up with several statements describing the character, without saying the character's name. These statements were incorporated into a riddle of sorts. However, the goal of this riddle was not to stump its readers, but to help them know exactly which character was being described. For example, if students were reading *Charlotte's Web*, the statements (riddle) describing Charlotte might be:

I saved a friend's life.
I created quite a stir with my evening's work.
I am not afraid of heights.
I have a soft spot for porcine pets.
I am a skilled weaver.

Who am I?

After writing and refining these riddles, students used construction paper and marking pens to make nice copies for placement on a bulletin board. The line with the question "Who am I?" was written on a narrow strip of different-colored construction paper that was as long as the larger piece of construction paper was wide. A piece of tape was put along the top of this strip and attached to the construction paper so that it served as a flap hiding the solution which was written at the bottom of the paper. The completed riddles were pinned to the bulletin board and students went there and read the riddles in their free time. After reading each riddle, they guessed the solution and lifted the flap to see if they were correct.

To adapt this activity to math, simply changed the final question to "What number am I?" Demonstrate the procedure by picking several numbers and writing five statements describing each number on the board as shown in the following example:

I am less than 100.
I am an even number.
My tens digit is five greater than my ones digit.
The sum of my two digits is nine.
I am the product of eight and nine.

What number am I?

After doing several examples like the one above together as a class, challenge groups of students to pick a number and create a number riddle describing that number. Go from group to group facilitating this process by giving hints when needed without doing students' thinking for them. This interaction will give you insight into students' thinking and help you assess their numeracy skills. After each group finishes writing a riddle, put it on the chalkboard for others to see. Solve

each of the riddles together as a class. During this process, students will see how other groups described their numbers, thereby exposing everyone in the class to a variety of mathematical language. After this introduction, individual students can construct their own number riddles. The completed riddles can be placed on the bulletin board along with the riddles from reading.

Three different sheets with riddles have been included that are aimed at different ability levels. Pick the riddles that are most appropriate for your students and either write them on the board or run off copies and give them to your students. These riddles are intended to be done in groups, but you may choose to give them to individual students instead. Be sure to monitor your students' work on solving the riddles. Spend time as a whole class discussing this process before asking students to create number riddles. When you sense that your students are ready to write their own riddles, hand out the last page which gives them

instructions on how to do this. You will need a supply of sticky notes for this section so that students can cover up their numbers. After they have written their riddles, they can trade papers with each other and try to solve other students' riddles. The riddles can then be placed on a bulletin board so that everyone has access to them.

The success of this activity will depend on your facilitation of it. Students need plenty of practice describing numbers using correct mathematical statements before they are asked to write number riddles. Students need to be reminded that a good riddle is one that leads the reader to the correct answer, not one that stumps the reader. Be sure to assess students' readiness before having them create their riddles. To make this process less intimidating, have groups write riddles and share them before asking individual students to do this. End this activity with a class discussion.

Digits in *Disguise*

Try to solve the following number riddles.
Show your work.

I am odd.
I am less than 10.
I am greater than 7.

I am even.
I am greater than 10.
I am less than 14.

I am between 5 and 12.
I am odd.
I have two digits.

Digits in *Disguise*

Try to solve the following number riddles.
Show your work.

I have two digits.
I am an odd number.
Both of my digits are the same.
I am greater than 80.

_____

I am a two-digit number.
I am less than 60.
My digits are consecutive numbers.
The sum of my digits is 11.

_____

I have three digits.
I am greater than 500 and less than 600.
My tens and ones digits are both the same even number.
The sum of all my digits is nine.

_____

Digits in Disguise

Try to solve the following number riddles. Show your work. You may need to use the back of the paper.

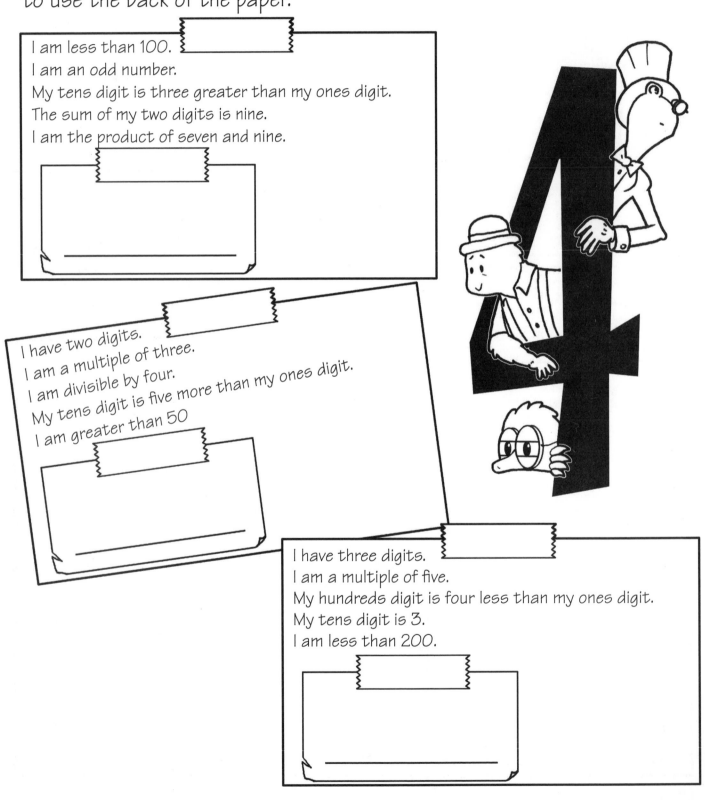

I am less than 100.
I am an odd number.
My tens digit is three greater than my ones digit.
The sum of my two digits is nine.
I am the product of seven and nine.

_____

I have two digits.
I am a multiple of three.
I am divisible by four.
My tens digit is five more than my ones digit.
I am greater than 50

_____

I have three digits.
I am a multiple of five.
My hundreds digit is four less than my ones digit.
My tens digit is 3.
I am less than 200.

_____

Digits in *Disguise*

Create a number riddle by following these instructions:

1. Choose a number for your riddle. Write it on the line at the bottom of the paper and cover it with a sticky note.

2. Write several clues describing your number on the lines provided.

3. Trade papers with a classmate and see if he or she can guess your number.

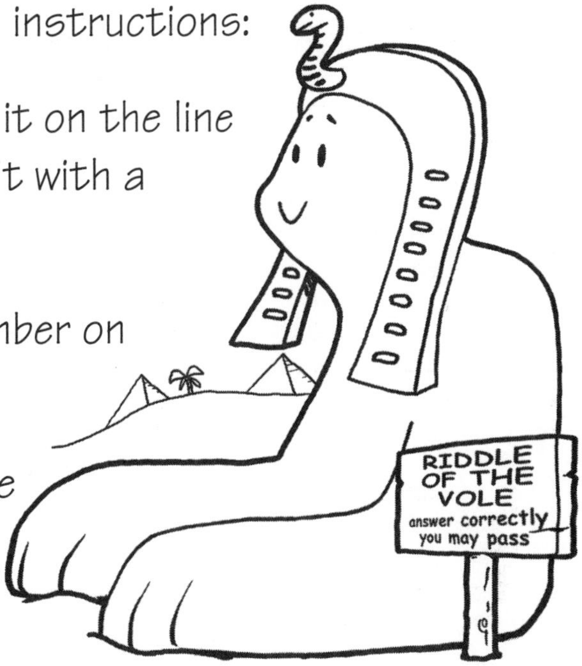

RIDDLE
OF THE
VOLE
answer correctly
you may pass

Clues
_____
_____
_____
_____
_____

What number am I?
_____

Topic
Whole Number Operations

Learning Goals
The students will:
1. identify problems to be solved in stories; and
2. solve problems using words, pictures, or symbols.

Guiding Document
NCTM Standards 2000*
- *Use multiple models to develop initial understandings of place value and the base-ten number system*
- *Develop a sense of whole numbers and represent and use them in flexible ways, including relating, composing, and decomposing numbers*
- *Connect number words and numerals to the quantities they represent, using various physical models and representations*
- *Understand various meanings of addition and subtraction of whole numbers and the relationship between the two operations*

Math
Whole number operations
   story problems

Integrated Processes
Observing
Comparing and contrasting
Relating
Communicating
Applying

Materials
For each group of students:
   two brown bags
   character page
   number page
   story problem pages
   crayon or highlighter pen

For the class:
   transparency (see *Management 2*)

Frank Frog

Background Information
Students often have a difficult time solving story problems. They may benefit from directed instruction that focuses their attention on the problem's components and what the problem is actually asking.

The problems presented in this experience are representative of the types often encountered by students. In each story, students are first asked to identify and underline the problem the story is asking them to solve. The blanks in the story will identify the characters involved as well as the numbers. The students will then be asked to show how they solved the problem. They can show their understanding of the problem in pictures, words, or in symbols. You will want to encourage the students to show their thinking in multiple ways.

Management
1. Prior to teaching this lesson make one set of bags for each group by gluing the labels for the *Characters* and *Numbers* on the bags. Cut out the individual characters and place them in the bag labeled *Characters*. The numbers will be placed in the *Numbers* bag. Each group will also need a set of story problems.
2. Prepare a transparency of the first problem for use on the overhead.
3. Students can work in groups of two to four students.
4. In several instances, students will need to place their selected numbers in an order that will avoid the use of negative numbers. They should not glue down any numbers until an order has been determined for them. Optional: If a selected number will not work in a given situation, have students draw another number or make up one of their own.

Procedure
1. Place the first story problem on the overhead and read with the students.

   ____ has a collection of _____ pebbles. _____ has collected____ pebbles. Who has the most pebbles?

2. Ask the students to first identify the problem they are trying to solve. (They should be able to relate that they are trying to find out who has the most pebbles.) After the students have identified the problem, underline the sentence that identifies what they are being asked to solve. Ask the students what else they need to know to be able to solve the problem. (The students should be able to identify that they need to know who has the pebbles and how many pebbles each one has.)

3. Distribute the brown bags. Have the students read the labels on the bags. Explain to them that these bags contain pictures of characters and numbers.
4. Ask, "Which of these bags would have something you need in order to solve the problem on the overhead?" (The students should be able to tell that they need something from the *Characters* bag and the *Numbers* bag.)
5. Ask them how many characters and numbers they need to be able to solve the problem. (The students should be able to relate that they need two characters and two numbers.)
6. Distribute a copy of the story you have on the overhead and tell the students to draw out two characters and two numbers from the bag and glue them in the correct location in the story.
7. Have each group solve the problem and share their answers. Tell them they will need to show their work in numbers, pictures, or words. Talk about why there were different answers. (The answer is dependent on who the characters are and what the numbers are.)
8. Tell the students they will now solve other problems. Distribute the story problems. They will then need to decide how many characters and numbers they will need by reading the problem. Remind them that they must first underline the problem and then show how they solved the problem using numbers, pictures, or words.
9. When all groups have finished, let groups share some of their stories and solutions.

Connecting Learning
1. What is the first step involved in solving a story problem? [Underlining the question you are trying to answer.]
2. How did you decide what went in each blank in the rebus story?
3. What three things do you need to know to be able to solve a story problem? [the question, the characters, and the numbers]
4. How are these three parts related to each other?
5. How did this activity help you become better at solving story problems?

Evidence of Learning
1. Check student sheets for underlining of the correct question in each problem.
2. Be sure the student explanations correctly solve the problem presented.

* Reprinted with permission from *Principles and Standards for School Mathematics*, 2000 by the National Council of Teachers of Mathematics. All rights reserved

Uncle Rebus Stories

1. _____ has a collection of _____ pebbles.

_____ has collected _____ pebbles. Who has the most pebbles?

Uncle Rebus Stories

2.

Yesterday at the pond, _____ counted _____ dragonflies.

When a bird flew overhead, _____ dragonflies flew away. How many were left?

Uncle Rebus Stories

3.

_____ and _____ were going on a picnic. They invited

_____ to go with them. They ate _____ oranges,

_____ apples, and _____ bananas. How many pieces of

fruit did they eat?

Uncle Rebus Stories

4.

In _____'s garden there are _____ flowers.

_____ are tulips. The rest are sunflowers. How many are sunflowers?

5.

Uncle Rebus Stories

It was a very warm day. ____ and ____ sold

____ glasses of lemonade from their stand in the morning and

____ glasses of lemonade in the afternoon. When did they sell the

most lemonade?

Uncle Rebus Stories

6.

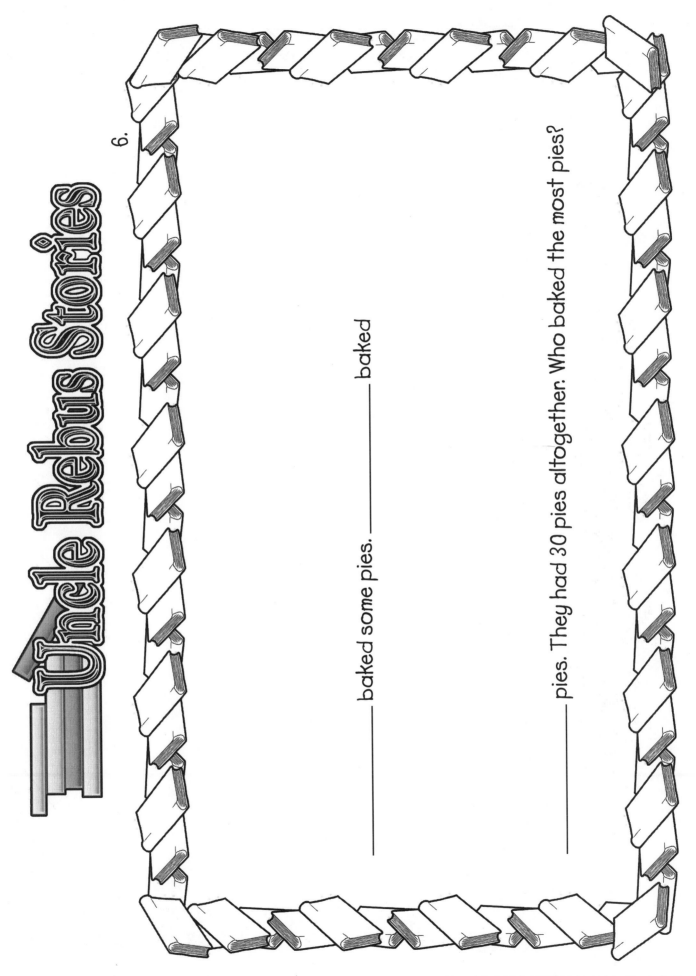

_____ baked

_____ baked some pies. _____

_____ pies. They had 30 pies altogether. Who baked the most pies?

Uncle Rebus Stories

7.

_____ had 50 nuts and 35 berries. He gave some nuts to _____, his best friend. Now he has _____ left. How many _____ did he give to his best friend?

Uncle Rebus Stories

8.

On a warm spring day ————————— , and ————————

went on a walk. They counted ———————— robins, ———————— blue

————————— birds, and ———————— squirrels. How many birds did they count?

Uncle Rebus Stories

9.

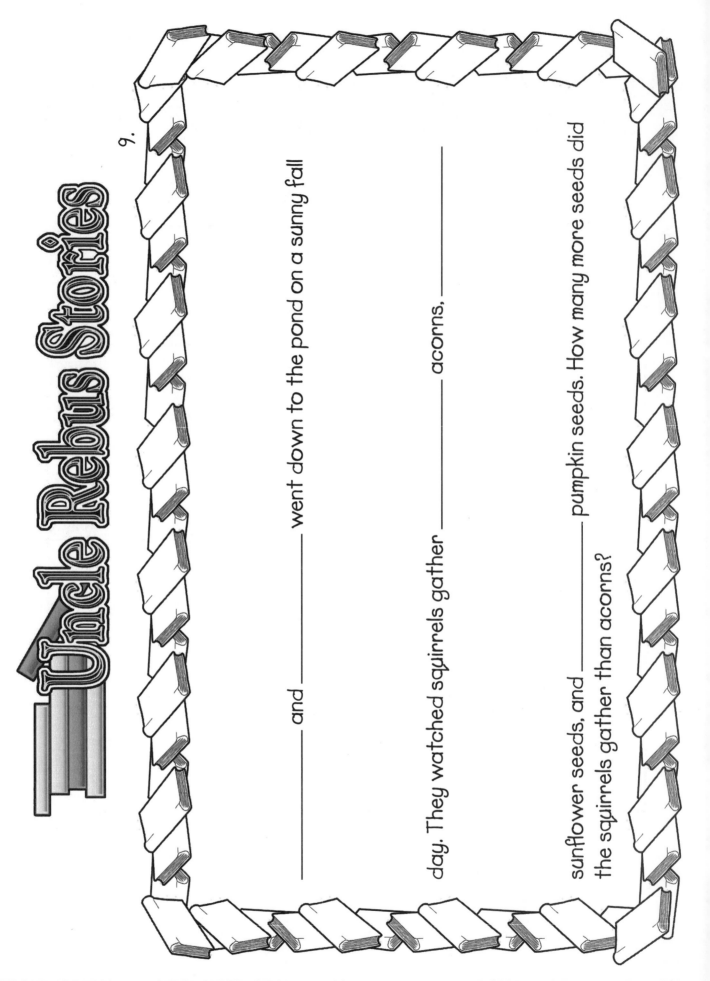

_____ and _____ went down to the pond on a sunny fall day. They watched squirrels gather _____ acorns, _____ sunflower seeds, and _____ pumpkin seeds. How many more seeds did the squirrels gather than acorns?

Uncle Rebus Stories

Major Mitchell Mole	Max Mole	Myrtle Mole	Marcia Mole	Malcolm Mole	Matilda Mole
Vinnie Vole	Victor Vole	Violet Vole	Vance Vole	Veronica Vole	Vivian Vole
Felecia Frog	Frank Frog	Sir Francis Frog	Foster Frog	Frieda Frog	Fiona Frog

32	14	7	4	12
56	24	17	9	10
19	48	25	38	41
20	35	73	66	2

Sharing and Solving Stories

These stories will give your students practice doing addition and subtraction problems that match situations in their daily lives. Several ideas are given, but you and/or your students can write and solve many more. Students become better problem solvers if they are given multiple opportunities and methods to solve problems. Students need time to talk and share their processes.

In these stories, the students are always first asked to identify the problem for each question. They are then asked to solve the problem and show their work using words, drawings, or numbers. The final thing they are asked to do is to be able to explain how they solved the problem.

Example
Today is the second of January. How many days have passed since it was Christmas? (Use this pattern for other holidays and events.)

- Identify the question.
- Solve the problem and show your work in words, drawings, or numbers.
- Be prepared to explain how you solved the problem.

The question is how many days have passed since it was Christmas. The students should be able to tell you that it has been eight days since Christmas. They could use a calendar to solve the problem. They can count on from the 25th of December until January 2nd. Whatever method they use, their explanations—written and oral—should reflect how they went about solving the problem. The shared strategies for solving problems should help all your students become better problem solvers.

Today is _____. _____'s birthday is on _____. How many more days until he or she will celebrate it?
(Example: Today is April 5th. Tyrese's birthday is April 18th. How many more days until he will celebrate his birthday?)

- Identify the question.
- Solve the problem and show your work in words, drawings, or numbers.
- Be prepared to explain how you solved the problem.

Today _____ students are buying their lunches and _____ students brought their lunches. How many more are buying than bringing lunches?

- Identify the question.
- Solve the problem and show your work in words, drawings, or numbers.
- Be prepared to explain how you solved the problem.

We went to the book fair yesterday. Keel bought seven books, Amber bought 11 books, and James bought eight books. How many books did the three students buy altogether?

- Identify the question.
- Solve the problem and show your work in words, drawings, or numbers.
- Be prepared to explain how you solved the problem.

Andrew had 25 cents before he went to school. He found some money on the way to school and now he has 87 cents. How much money did he find?

- Identify the question.
- Solve the problem and show your work in words, drawings, or numbers.
- Be prepared to explain how you solved the problem.
- What coins could he have found?

Michelle and David baked cookies for the school's bake sale. Michelle baked 48. They had a total of 84 to sell. How many cookies did David bake?

- Identify the question.
- Solve the problem and show your work in words, drawings, or numbers.
- Be prepared to explain how you solved the problem.

Juan has a collection of 32 stamps. Sarah has 26 stamps in her collection. Sadie has 17 stamps in hers. How many stamps to they have altogether?

- Identify the question.
- Solve the problem and show your work in words, drawings, or numbers.
- Be prepared to explain how you solved the problem.

James and Janna went to the zoo this past weekend. They saw 17 birds, 14 snakes, and 12 lizards. How many more birds did they see than lizards?

- Identify the question.
- Solve the problem and show your work in words, drawings, or numbers.
- Be prepared to explain how you solved the problem.

The class library has 100 books. Marla checked out eight and Jeff checked out four. How many books are left in the library?

- Identify the question.
- Solve the problem and show your work in words, drawings, or numbers.
- Be prepared to explain how you solved the problem.

Playful and Intelligent Practice

- **Meaning and understanding must precede practice.**
  Students should be able to provide both physical and mathematical evidence that they understand an arithmetic fact before they are asked to memorize the corresponding symbolic basic fact. Look for this evidence in more than one setting.

- **Students should begin to memorize basic arithmetic facts soon after they demonstrate an understanding of symbolic statements.**
  Use concrete materials then move to pictures and models in the initial stages of instruction. There comes a time when a student is expected to use symbols (written numerals) to represent the mathematical ideas and basic facts.

- **Students need daily practice.**
  It is not uncommon to see students hurry through a drill session by figuring out answers. They rapidly count on their fingers, or quickly make tally marks and count. These students are not practicing remembering basic facts, they are practicing finger counting or tallying, and they become very good at these procedures. However, the purpose of the playful and intelligent practice is to commit the basic facts to memory and to work toward this goal, not to use other counting methods to remember the answers.

  During practice sessions, do not take time to work out or explain answers. The students should have this understanding before beginning the session.

  Keep the practice session short—five to ten minutes. Two or three five-minute practice sessions a day will enable children to memorize basic facts.

  Try to focus on only a few basic facts in a given lesson, and always review previously memorized facts. Generally, three or four new facts are a challenge that most students will accept. Even after mastery is attained, review should be continued throughout the primary grades.

  Vary the activities using games, flash cards, oral practice, story telling with storyboards, and more. Keep the sessions enthusiastic and interesting. Praise students for good effort and keep a record of their progress.

- **Use tables and charts to introduce students to patterns in the numeration system.**

—Larry Ecklund

Topic
Basic Addition/Subtraction Facts

Key Question
How can a triangle help you learn your basic addition and subtraction facts?

Learning Goals
Students will:
1. read an addition/subtraction chart,
2. become aware of the commutative property for addition but that does not exist for subtraction, and
2. create a personal set of addition and subtraction cards for facts they need to memorize.

Guiding Document
NCTM Standards 2000*
- *Develop and use strategies for whole number computations, with a focus on addition and subtraction*
- *Develop fluency with basic number combinations for addition and subtraction*

Math
Operations
    addition
    subtraction

Integrated Processes
Observing
Recording
Comparing and contrasting
Communicating
Applying

Materials
For each student:
    index cards (see *Management 1*)
    Addition/Subtraction Facts Table
    scissors
    Corner Tool (see *Management 2*)

Background Information
There are 100 basic facts for addition and 100 for subtraction. The focus of this activity is to give students a concrete way to see the relationship between addition and subtraction and to focus on the basic facts they do not know. They will construct a tool that will help them learn their basic facts. The students will use this tool to help them develop a better understanding of the commutative property of addition (The Commutative Property of Addition: two whole numbers can be added in either order, a + b or b + a.) as well as the realization that there is not a commutative property for subtraction.

Management
1. The students will need one 5" x 8" index card for every two triangle cards they construct. It is suggested that students only construct cards for the facts on which they need to work.
2. Copy the *Corner Tool* page onto card stock. Each corner tool is made with two strips which are taped or glued together as illustrated. Copy the *Transparency Templates*. Cut the squares apart. Tape the transparent piece to the back of the *Corner Tool* as illustrated.

Procedure
1. Ask the *Key Question* and state the *Learning Goals*.
2. Distribute the *Addition/Subtraction Facts Table*.
3. Guide the students in searching for patterns in the table. Help them see that it has a line of symmetry that runs diagonally from the upper left to bottom right corners.
4. Discuss with the students some of the patterns they discovered.

5. Distribute the assembled *Corner Tools*. Demonstrate how to use the tool to find the addition facts. Ask the students, "Where is the sum (answer) for an addition problem always located?" [It is always located in the corner.]

6. Demonstrate how to use the tool to find subtraction facts by placing the transparent piece over the minuend and one arm over the subtrahend or the difference. Ask the students where the difference (the answer) for a subtraction problem is? [It is located at one of the ends of the corner tool.] Ask the students how this is different from addition facts. Help the students see that the order for addition does not matter, but the order for subtraction does matter. Relate this to the commutative property of addition.

7. Direct each student to locate a fact on the *Addition/Subtraction Facts Table* they are having difficulty learning.

8. Distribute the index cards and scissors. Demonstrate how to cut the card to create two triangles.

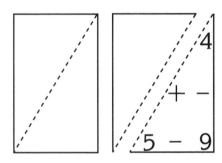

9. Direct them to record the digit next to the corner of the *Corner Tool* in the corner of the index card that forms the right angle. Record the numbers that are at the end of each arm of the *Corner Tool*, one in each of the other two angles of the card.

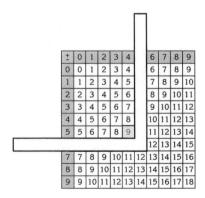

10. Ask the students to create cards for each fact for which they are having difficulty.

Connecting Learning

1. Tell how addition and subtraction are related.
2. How do the triangle flashcards help you learn your facts faster?
3. What does the commutative property of addition mean?
4. Why is it important to know your basic addition and subtraction facts?

Evidence of Learning

1. Listen as students explain how addition and subtraction are related.
2. Watch as students construct the triangle cards. Check for correct placement of the numbers and symbols.

* Reprinted with permission from *Principles and Standards for School Mathematics*, 2000 by the National Council of Teachers of Mathematics. All rights reserved.

Transparency Templates

CORNERING the FACTS

Corner Tools

100 Addition/Subtraction Facts Table

±	0	1	2	3	4	5	6	7	8	9
0	0	1	2	3	4	5	6	7	8	9
1	1	2	3	4	5	6	7	8	9	10
2	2	3	4	5	6	7	8	9	10	11
3	3	4	5	6	7	8	9	10	11	12
4	4	5	6	7	8	9	10	11	12	13
5	5	6	7	8	9	10	11	12	13	14
6	6	7	8	9	10	11	12	13	14	15
7	7	8	9	10	11	12	13	14	15	16
8	8	9	10	11	12	13	14	15	16	17
9	9	10	11	12	13	14	15	16	17	18

Purpose of the Game
Students will explore the addition and subtraction table

Materials
For each group of four students:
   50 index cards, 3" x 5"
   4 colored markers (see *Management 1*)
   scissors
   addition and subtraction table

Management
1. Each member in a group needs to use the same color marker.
2. The students will need to place a line under the number 9 so that it can be distinguished from the number 6.

Procedure
Part One
1. Direct the students to cut the addition and subtraction table along the bold lines. This will divide the table into four equal parts.
2. Tell each student to select one of the four sections of the table that has been cut apart.
3. Demonstrate how to fold one of the index cards in half and cut it apart. Tell students that they will need to fold and cut the 50 cards that their group was given.

4. After each group has cut the cards, tell them to divide them equally within their group.
5. Direct each student to copy the numbers from the section of the addition/subtraction table they have onto the index cards they prepared. Show them how to draw a line under any nine so that the students will be able to distinguish the difference between a six and a 9.

Part Two
1. Tell the students the object of the game is to build the addition and subtraction table.
2. Direct one student in each group to shuffle and deal the cards to the students in the group. Each student will have 25 cards.
3. Play begins with the student on the left of the dealer. He or she may place any card on the table.
4. Play continues clockwise around the table. The student may only play a card that will touch the card played on the table. The card may share an edge or a diagonal corner. If there are no plays, the student skips a turn and play continues clockwise.

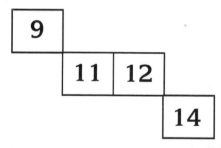

5. The winner is the one who is able to play all of his or her cards first.
6. After the students have completely constructed the addition and subtraction table, discuss strategies they used as well as patterns they discovered.

0	1	2	3	4	5	6	7	8	9
1	2	3	4	5	6	7	8	9	10
2	3	4	5	6	7	8	9	10	11
3	4	5	6	7	8	9	10	11	12
4	5	6	7	8	9	10	11	12	13
5	6	7	8	9	10	11	12	13	14
6	7	8	9	10	11	12	13	14	15
7	8	9	10	11	12	13	14	15	16
8	9	10	11	12	13	14	15	16	17
9	10	11	12	13	14	15	16	17	18

Purpose of the Game
Students will play a card game that challenges them to use mental math to find equations that equal even sums between 10 and 18.

Materials
Make It Even cards, one set per student

Management
1. This game can be played with even target sums ranging from 10 to 18. (Games can also be played with target sums lower than 10, but the smaller the sum, the fewer the cards and the shorter the game.)
2. Each student will need a set of *Make It Even* cards. These cards should be copied onto card stock and laminated for durability. These cards can also be ordered from AIMS.
3. The target sum will determine the cards which students need to use. Look at the table below to help you determine which cards to use with your students. *Note: When using card sets that begin with 1, 1, no cards with a zero can be in the set, even if they have a sum that is greater than 1, 1. Likewise, no cards containing a 7, 8, or 9 may be used in a set that ends with 6, 6, even if their sum is less than 6, 6.*

Target Sum	Cards
18	All
16	0/0 to 8/8 or 1/1 to 7/7
14	0/0 to 7/7 or 1/1 to 6/6 or 2/2 to 9/9
12	0/0 to 6/6 or 1/1 to 5/5
10	0/0 to 5/5

Rules
1. Have students shuffle their *Make It Even* cards and lay them face up on the desk, in stacks of two. There should always be one extra card, which can be placed on any of the stacks. For example, if students were playing with the cards 0, 0 to 5, 5 (target sum = 10), they would have ten stacks, as shown below.

2. The object is to match cards that total the target sum. For example, with the illustrated cards, the 5, 5 and the 0, 0 are a pair; the 4, 2 and the 4, 0 are a pair; the 5, 2 and the 2, 1 are a pair, and so on. When students see a pair of cards that total the target sum, those two cards are removed from the stacks and set aside.
3. Students continue to pair and remove cards until only one card is left. If students should get to a place where none of the visible cards pair up to total the target sum, they may move the top card from one stack into any empty space.
4. If students have correctly paired the cards, the one remaining card will always be one-half the target sum. For example, if the target sum is 16, the final card will have a sum of eight. If the target sum is 10, the final card will have a sum of five, and so on.
5. Once students have had a chance to play the game several times, add the additional challenge of time. Play "Beat the Clock," and have students race to see if they can finish the game within a set amount of time.

Variation
A two person version of this game can be played in a more competitive format. In pairs, have students shuffle one set of *Make It Even* cards and lay out nine cards, face up, in three rows of three. As students see two cards that add up to the target sum, they call out "Sum." They then remove the two cards that they saw, stating the addition problem out loud. If the target sum is 14, a student might say, "Five and five is 10, three and one is four, 10 and four is 14." The removed cards are replaced by two more from the deck, and the game continues until all of the cards have been dealt and the pairs have been made. The player with the most pairs at the end of the game is the winner.

Extension
Experiment with different sets of cards for the various target sums (e.g., use 0, 0 to 7, 7 for a target sum of 14; or 0, 0 to 6, 6 for a target sum of 12). Which sets can you get to work? Are they still self-checking? Why or why not?

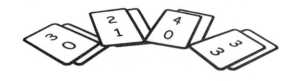

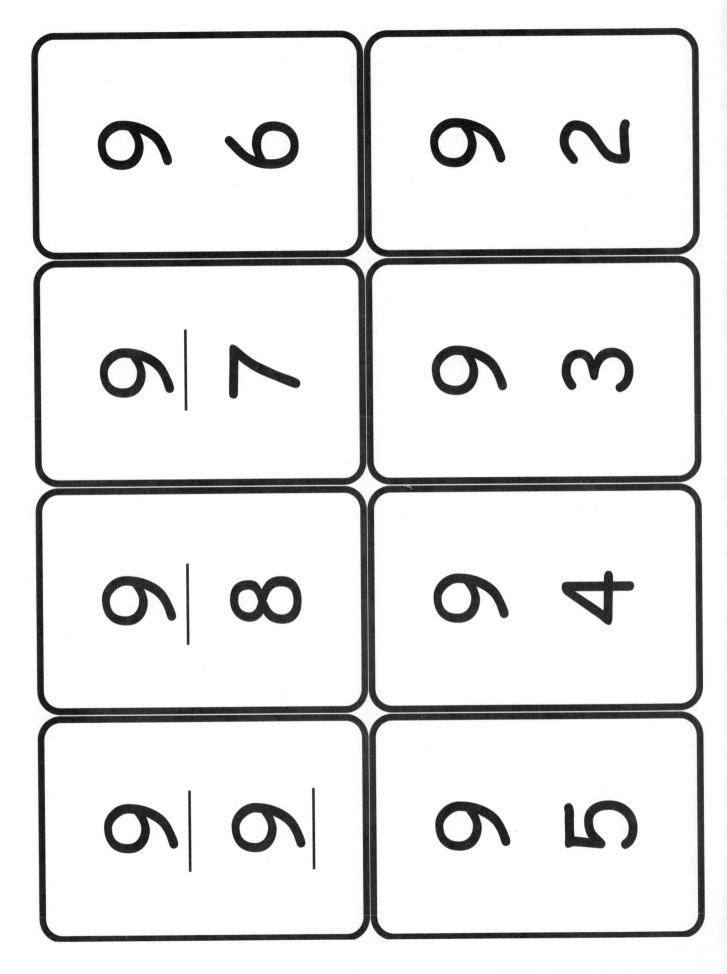

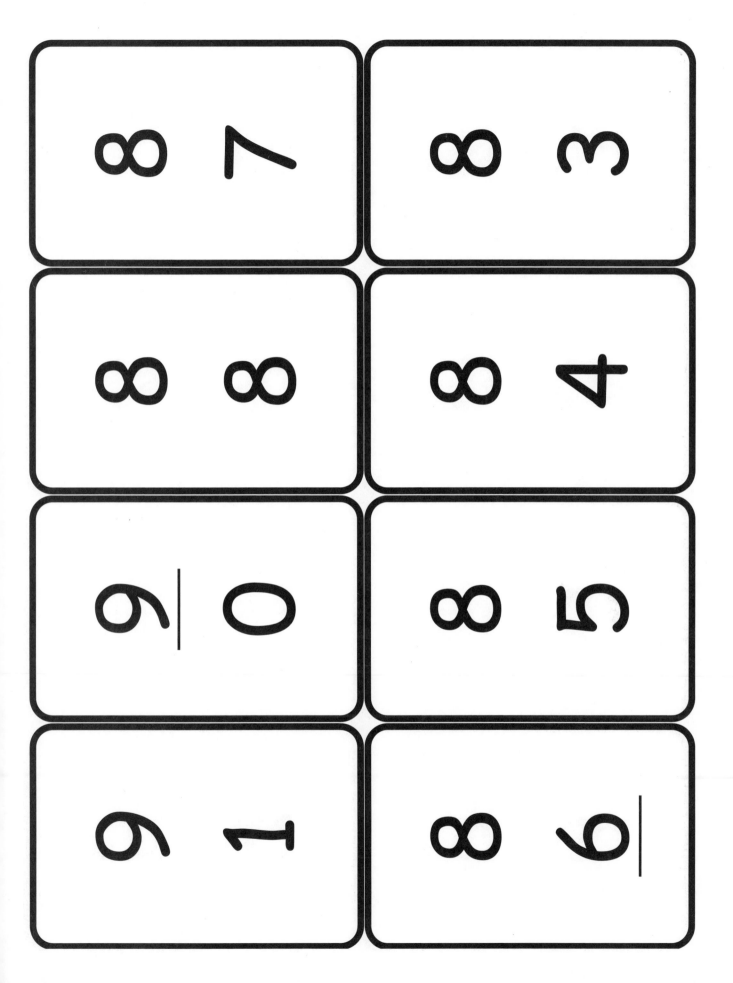

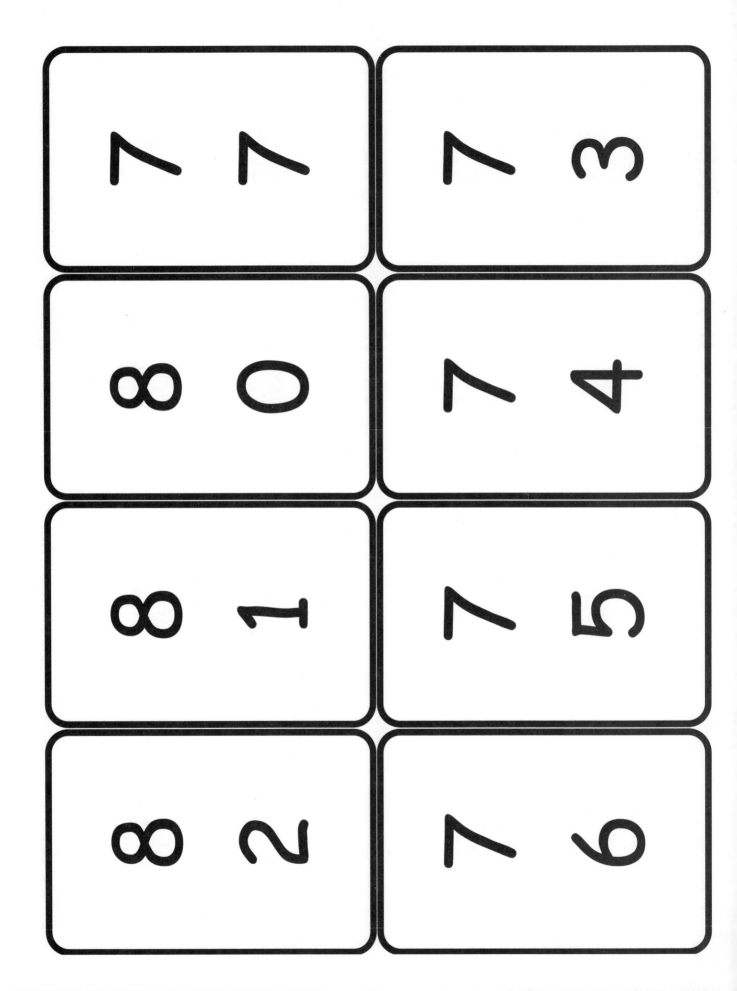

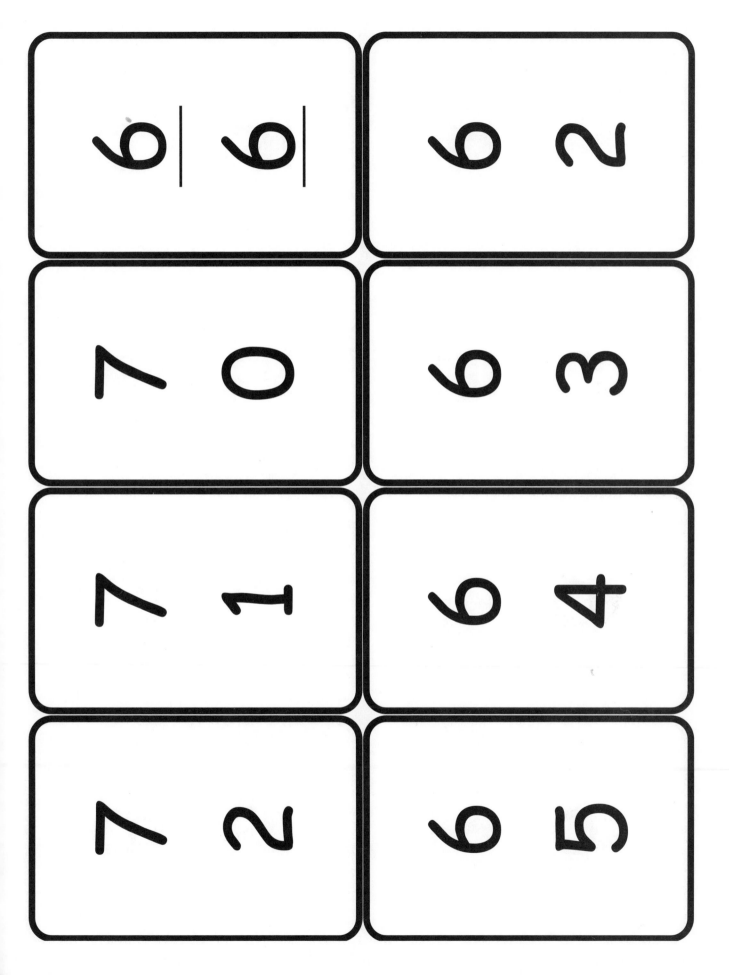

5 4	5 0
5 5	5 1
6 — 0	5 2
6 1	5 3

4 1	3 1
4 2	3 2
4 3	3 3
4 4	4 0

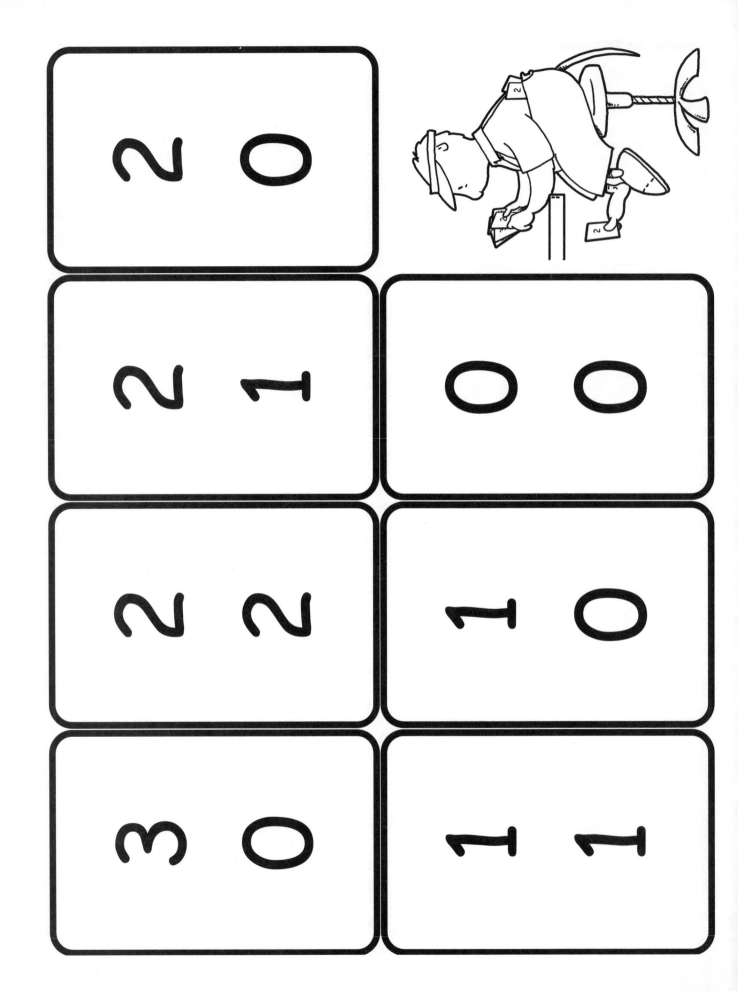

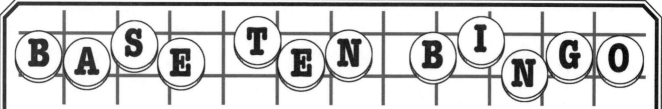

BASE TEN BINGO

Distribute a 0–99 chart to each student and markers for covering. As clues are read, students may cover one number (only one) that is a correct response to the clue. The first student to cover five in a row in any direction calls out "bingo."

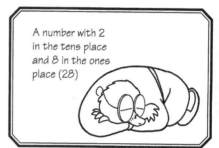

A number with 2 in the tens place and 8 in the ones place (28)

1. A number between 52 and 58 (53, 54, 55, 56, 57)
2. A number with 2 in the tens place and 8 in the ones place (28)
3. A number that has the same number of tens as ones (11, 22, 33, 44, 55, 66, 77, 88, 99)
4. An even number with one in the tens place (10, 12, 14, 16, 18)
5. 4 tens plus 6 (46)
6. 10 more than 15 (25)
7. 10 less than 47 (37)
8. 6 ones and 20 (26)
9. An odd number with 4 in the tens place (41, 43, 45, 47, 49)

3 tens and 5 ones (35)

10. 3 tens and 5 ones (35)
11. Twice as many tens as ones (21, 42, 63, 84)
12. A number with an even number of tens and an odd number of ones (21, 23, 25, 27, 29, 41, 43, 45, 47, 49, 61, 63, 65, 67, 69, 81, 83, 85, 87, 89)
13. Free Choice
14. A number with an even number in the ones place (Any number that ends in a 0, 2, 4, 6, or 8)
15. A number greater than 4 tens (any number greater than 40)
16. A number less than 6 tens (any number less than 60)
17. 8 tens and 9 ones (89)

18. 50 tens plus 7 ones (57)
19. An even number (any even number)
20. An odd number (any odd number)
21. A number with a 5 in the ones place (5, 15, 25, 35, 45, 55, 65, 75, 85, 95)
22. 3 tens minus 9 ones (21)
23. An odd number with a 7 in the ones place (17, 27, 37, 47, 57, 67, 77, 87, 97)
24. 4 ones plus 6 ones plus 9 ones (19)
25. 2 tens minus 9 ones (11)

50 tens plus 7 ones (57)

26. 2 tens and 7 ones plus 3 ones (30)
27. An even number less than 5 tens (any even number less than 49)
28. An odd number greater than 6 tens and 7 ones (any odd number greater than 68)
29. 7 tens and 4 ones (74)
30. 9 tens and 8 ones plus 1 (99)
Two cards are blank for your own clues.

BASE TEN BINGO

0	1	2	3	4	5	6	7	8	9
10	11	12	13	14	15	16	17	18	19
20	21	22	23	24	25	26	27	28	29
30	31	32	33	34	35	36	37	38	39
40	41	42	43	44	45	46	47	48	49
50	51	52	53	54	55	56	57	58	59
60	61	62	63	64	65	66	67	68	69
70	71	72	73	74	75	76	77	78	79
80	81	82	83	84	85	86	87	88	89
90	91	92	93	94	95	96	97	98	99

A number between 52 and 58 (53, 54, 55, 56, 57)

A number with 2 in the tens place and 8 in the ones place (28)

A number that has the same number of tens as ones (11, 22, 33, 44, 55, 66, 77, 88, 99)

An even number with one in the tens place (10, 12, 14, 16, 18)

4 tens plus 6 (46)

10 more than 15 (25)

10 less than 47 (37)

6 ones and 20 (26)

An odd number with 4 in the tens place (41, 43, 45, 47, 49)

3 tens and 5 ones (35)

Twice as many tens as ones (21, 42, 63, 84)

A number with an even number of tens and an odd number of ones (21, 23, 25, 27, 29, 41, 43, 45, 47, 49, 61, 63, 65, 67, 69, 81, 83, 85, 87, 89)

Free Choice

A number with an even number in the ones place (Any number that ends in a 0, 2, 4, 6, or 8)

A number greater than 4 tens (any number greater than 40)

A number less than 6 tens (any number less than 60)

8 tens and
9 ones (89)

50 tens plus
7 ones (57)

An even number
(any even number)

An odd number
(any odd number)

A number with
a 5 in the ones
place (5, 15, 25,
35, 45, 55, 65,
75, 85, 95)

3 tens minus
9 ones (21)

An odd number
with a 7 in the
ones place (17,
27, 37, 47, 57,
67, 77, 87, 97)

4 ones plus 6
ones plus 9
ones (19)

2 tens minus
9 ones (11)

2 tens and
7 ones plus
3 ones (30)

An even
number less
than 5 tens
(any even
number less
than 49)

An odd number
greater than 6 tens
and 7 ones (any
odd number greater
than 68)

7 tens and 4
ones (74)

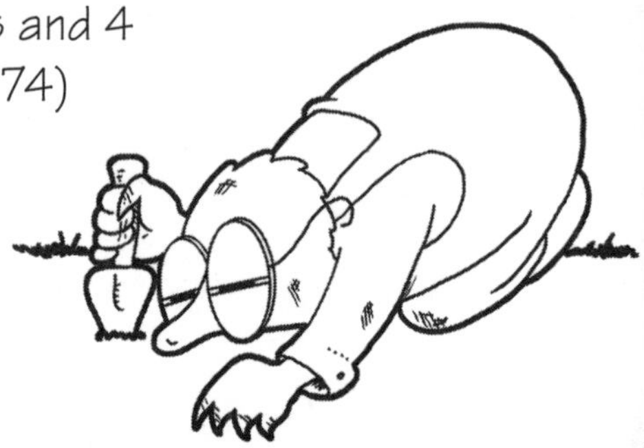

9 tens and 8
ones plus 1 (99)

Blockout! brings a problem-solving approach to intensive practice with basic addition facts at three levels of difficulty. Students "block out" combinations of two or more addends whose sum equals a target number. Target numbers range from 7 to 20. The three levels of difficulty are provided by cards with 9, 16, and 25 addends that need to be formed into sets.

Features

Blockout! possesses unique characteristics that are highly desirable in practicing basic addition facts.

- Each problem is largely self-correcting. Self-correction reduces need for teacher intervention. This feature results from requiring that all squares on the game board must be covered correctly to arrive at the desired sum.

- Practice extends finding the sum of two numbers to those involving three and four addends.

- Mental rather than paper and pencil calculation is practiced. Searching for appropriate addends builds facility with "scanning," a process in which sums are quickly determined through mental calculation.

- Careful progression of difficulty allows the teacher to prescribe practice at a specific level of difficulty or with specific addends. More difficult combinations receive more intensive practice.

- Emphasis on problem solving is built into the activity by requiring specific combinations of addends to cover the game board. Certain combinations, while correct in themselves, will not satisfy this requirement.

- The activity is versatile so that it can be used for individual, small group, or total class practice.

- A positive attitude toward mathematics is facilitated in that only the correct solution survives without trace of error. The result is strong positive reinforcement and pride in one's work. Use of colored tiles permits the child to correct a false move without leaving any record of the mistake.

Rules and Procedures

The card number identifies the target sum. (The example which follows has a target sum of 10.) The object is to identify sets of addends totaling this target sum in such a manner that all addends are used. If any squares remain uncovered, the correct solution has not been achieved even though each set of addends may total the target sum correctly.

Each addend in a set must have a common boundary with another addend; touching corners does not fulfill this requirement. All the addends in a set will form a chain of some sort: I-shaped, L-shaped, T-shaped, etc.

A set is composed of two or more addends. When a set of addends is identified, all members in that set should be covered with tiles of a given color. The transparent tiles permit students to check each set without removing any markers. No more than four colors are ever required to keep each of the sets distinct from the others.

Problem solving is an integral part of this activity. As students move progressively through the sequence of cards, their skill in identifying addends and fully covering the game board will develop significantly.

The sum and difficulty level of each card is identified by its name. Thus, a card labeled "7a" will have a target sum of 7 and will be the least difficult in the sequence; "7d" will be the most difficult.

Example: Card 10b

The target sum in this example is 10. The combinations of the addends 5, 2, and 3 equals 10, so it qualifies as a set. However, the student must decide which 3 to combine with the 5 and 2, since two 3s have a common boundary with the 5 and 2 set and would qualify. If 3 in the first row is used, it isolates the 4 in the first row by leaving it without neighbors to form a sum of 10. So 5 + 2 + 3 in the top two rows are covered with one color. Now begins the search for another set of addends with a sum of 10. The set 7 + 3 qualifies because it equals 10, but should the 3 in the second row or the 3 in the third row be used? The only choice that will provide full covering of the game board is the 3 in the third row. If the 3 in the second row is used, the 3 and 4 in the first row are isolated. (The sense of satisfaction comes when adding the final uncovered set—the target sum is achieved.)

Suggestions for Use

To prepare the activities for classroom use, duplicate the masters on card stock. The cards can then be laminated for longer life. Provide each student or group with sets of colored tiles as required by the number of addends on the card. The activity can be used in the following ways:

Individual Prescription

A student diagnosed as having trouble with certain addends is given an appropriate card with a suitable level of challenge on which to practice alone. The difficulty level is gradually increased until the desired level of competency is achieved.

Games in Pairs

Each child is supplied with tiles of a given color. Students take turns identifying sets with the tiles. If a child makes a mistake, the incorrect set of tiles must be removed and the turn is ended. Play ends when no further sets can be covered. Because of the approach in placing tiles under these rules, not all of the numbers will be covered. The player who has placed the most tiles on the card is the winner.

Full Class

A transparency is prepared. In one variation, two teams are formed. The two teams play competitively under the same rules as under "Games in Pairs." Teams alternate in forming sets. If a team makes an error that is detected by the other team, the turn is forfeited and the chips involved are removed.

One way to decide the winner is to award victory to the team covering the most spaces. To emphasize the addition of more difficult facts, however, the team having the most sets but covering the fewest average number of spaces is the winner.

Under a second approach, the entire class works together to find a way to cover all of the spaces on the board.

7a

4	1	3
1	2	4
6	5	2

7b

2	5	1
3	4	6
4	1	2

7c

3	4	4
2	2	1
5	1	6

7d

1	1	2	5
6	2	1	6
1	3	4	3
2	5	3	4

BLOCKOUT! Tiles

as seen on TV

10a

2	8	7	9	1
4	1	2	5	5
1	5	3	4	3
4	3	5	3	1
6	2	3	7	6

10b

9	1	5	3	4
4	3	2	7	3
4	2	8	3	4
2	7	2	1	6
2	1	8	4	5

BLOCKOUT! Tiles
as seen on TV

15a

5	5	9	6	7
7	5	3	4	8
4	3	8	6	6
4	9	3	3	2
8	2	5	9	4

15b

6	7	8	6	1
7	1	7	7	8
2	5	7	3	3
9	6	6	4	8
4	7	4	5	4

BLOCKOUT!
Tiles
as seen on TV

20a

6	4	9
5	8	7
9	8	4

20b

7	6	8
5	6	8
8	3	9

20c

9	2	9
6	7	5
7	7	8

20d

7	6	7	8
6	2	7	5
9	5	6	7
5	6	8	6

Who has...?
Addition and Subtraction

Elementary students benefit from revisiting basic skills through repeated experiences in a variety of formats. While the adage *practice makes perfect* makes sense to us, there is considerable support for the idea that "drilling" for periods longer than 10 minutes a day may be counterproductive.

This learning game provides playful and intelligent practice within a very short period of time. The game features:

- an element of "playfulness,"
- minimum teacher preparation,
- time efficiency,
- mental stimulation and exercise,
- student interest and motivation, and
- 100 percent accuracy.

Management
1. Copy a set of cards on card stock.
2. Laminate the cards for durability.

Procedure
1. Distribute one card to each student or pair of students.
2. Begin with any card.
3. Begin the game by reading a card (for example: "I have 17. Who that number plus 2?")
4. Direct the student holding the card with the correct response (19, in the case of the example) to read his or her card ("I have 19. Who has …").
5. Continue the game until the cycle returns to the beginning card.

Who Has? Addition and Subtraction Key

1. I have 17. Who has this number plus 2?
2. I have 19. Who has this number minus 8?
3. I have 11. Who has this number minus 5?
4. I have 6. Who has this number plus 4?
5. I have 10. Who has this number plus 6?
6. I have 16. Who has this number minus 7?
7. I have 9. Who has this number minus 8?
8. I have 1. Who has this number plus 6?
9. I have 7. Who has this number plus 6?
10. I have 13. Who has this number minus 11?
11. I have 2. Who has this number plus 13?
12. I have 15. Who has this number minus 7?
13. I have 8. Who has this number minus 5?
14. I have 3. Who has this number plus 11?
15. I have 14. Who has this number minus 2?
16. I have 12. Who has this number minus 7?
17. I have 5. Who has this number plus 13?
18. I have 18. Who has this number minus 14?
19. I have 4. Who has this number minus 4?
20. I have 0. Who has this number plus 17?

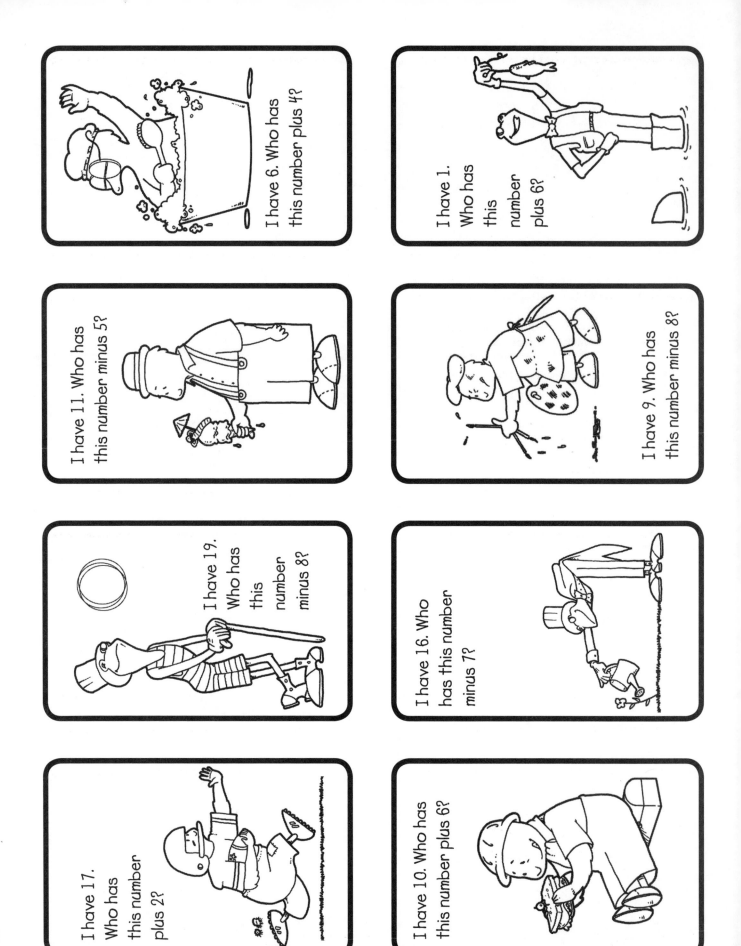

I have 6. Who has this number plus 4?

I have 1. Who has this number plus 6?

I have 11. Who has this number minus 5?

I have 9. Who has this number minus 8?

I have 19. Who has this number minus 8?

I have 16. Who has this number minus 7?

I have 17. Who has this number plus 2?

I have 10. Who has this number plus 6?

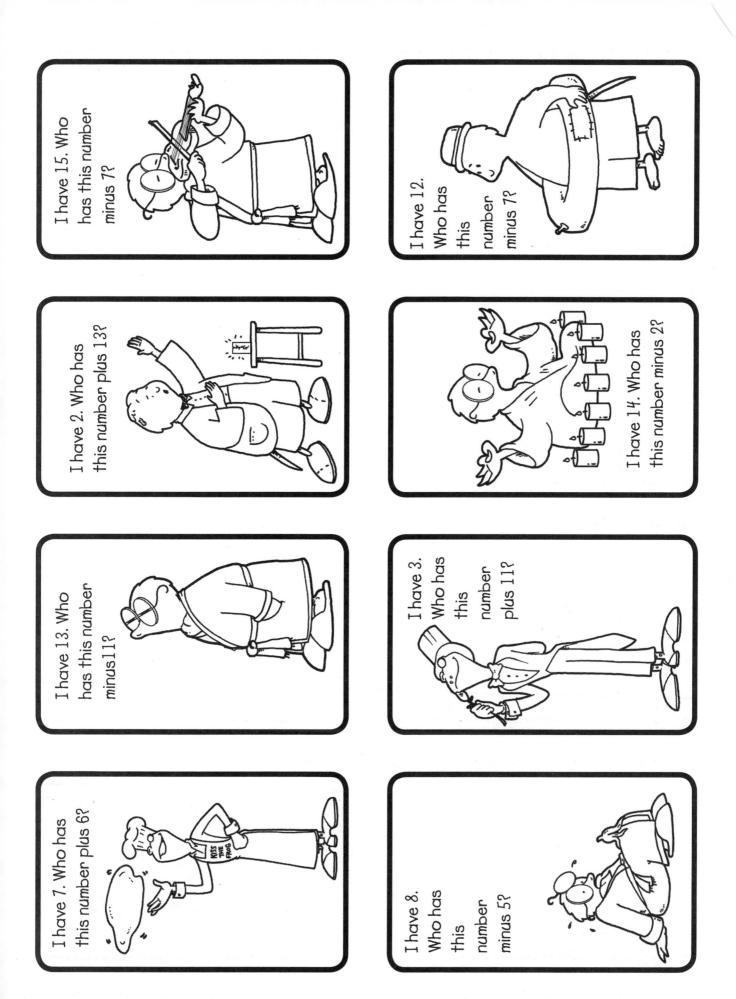

I have 15. Who has this number minus 7?

I have 12. Who has this number minus 7?

I have 2. Who has this number plus 13?

I have 14. Who has this number minus 2?

I have 13. Who has this number minus 11?

I have 3. Who has this number plus 11?

I have 7. Who has this number plus 6?

I have 8. Who has this number minus 5?

I have 0.
Who has
this
number
plus 17?

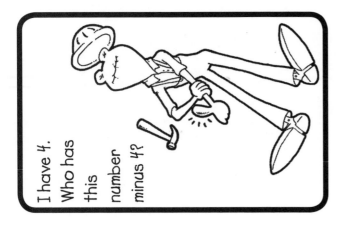

I have 18.
Who has
this
number
minus 14?

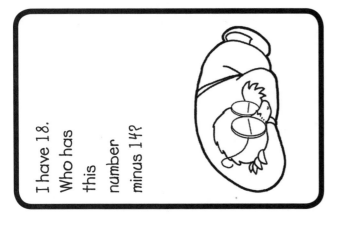

I have 4.
Who has
this
number
minus 4?

I have 5. Who
has this number
plus 13?

The AIMS Program

AIMS is the acronym for "**A**ctivities **I**ntegrating **M**athematics and **S**cience." Such integration enriches learning and makes it meaningful and holistic. AIMS began as a project of Fresno Pacific University to integrate the study of mathematics and science in grades K-9, but has since expanded to include language arts, social studies, and other disciplines.

AIMS is a continuing program of the non-profit AIMS Education Foundation. It had its inception in a National Science Foundation funded program whose purpose was to explore the effectiveness of integrating mathematics and science. The project directors in cooperation with 80 elementary classroom teachers devoted two years to a thorough field-testing of the results and implications of integration.

The approach met with such positive results that the decision was made to launch a program to create instructional materials incorporating this concept. Despite the fact that thoughtful educators have long recommended an integrative approach, very little appropriate material was available in 1981 when the project began. A series of writing projects have ensued and today the AIMS Education Foundation is committed to continue the creation of new integrated activities on a permanent basis.

The AIMS program is funded through the sale of this developing series of books and proceeds from the Foundation's endowment. All net income from program and products flows into a trust fund administered by the AIMS Education Foundation. Use of these funds is restricted to support of research, development, and publication of new materials. Writers donate all their rights to the Foundation to support its on-going program. No royalties are paid to the writers.

The rationale for integration lies in the fact that science, mathematics, language arts, social studies, etc., are integrally interwoven in the real world from which it follows that they should be similarly treated in the classroom where we are preparing students to live in that world. Teachers who use the AIMS program give enthusiastic endorsement to the effectiveness of this approach.

Science encompasses the art of questioning, investigating, hypothesizing, discovering, and communicating. Mathematics is a language that provides clarity, objectivity, and understanding. The language arts provide us powerful tools of communication. Many of the major contemporary societal issues stem from advancements in science and must be studied in the context of the social sciences. Therefore, it is timely that all of us take seriously a more holistic mode of educating our students. This goal motivates all who are associated with the AIMS Program. We invite you to join us in this effort.

Meaningful integration of knowledge is a major recommendation coming from the nation's professional science and mathematics associations. The American Association for the Advancement of Science in *Science for All Americans* strongly recommends the integration of mathematics, science, and technology. The National Council of Teachers of Mathematics places strong emphasis on applications of mathematics such as are found in science investigations. AIMS is fully aligned with these recommendations.

Extensive field testing of AIMS investigations confirms these beneficial results.

1. Mathematics becomes more meaningful, hence more useful, when it is applied to situations that interest students.
2. The extent to which science is studied and understood is increased, with a significant economy of time, when mathematics and science are integrated.
3. There is improved quality of learning and retention, supporting the thesis that learning which is meaningful and relevant is more effective.
4. Motivation and involvement are increased dramatically as students investigate real-world situations and participate actively in the process.

We invite you to become part of this classroom teacher movement by using an integrated approach to learning and sharing any suggestions you may have. The AIMS Program welcomes you!

AIMS Education Foundation Programs

A Day with AIMS®

Intensive one-day workshops are offered to introduce educators to the philosophy and rationale of AIMS. Participants will discuss the methodology of AIMS and the strategies by which AIMS principles may be incorporated into curriculum. Each participant will take part in a variety of hands-on AIMS investigations to gain an understanding of such aspects as the scientific/mathematical content, classroom management, and connections with other curricular areas. *A Day with AIMS®* workshops may be offered anywhere in the United States. Necessary supplies and take-home materials are usually included in the enrollment fee.

A Week with AIMS®

Throughout the nation, AIMS offers many one-week workshops each year, usually in the summer. Each workshop lasts five days and includes at least 30 hours of AIMS hands-on instruction. Participants are grouped according to the grade level(s) in which they are interested. Instructors are members of the AIMS Instructional Leadership Network. Supplies for the activities and a generous supply of take-home materials are included in the enrollment fee. Sites are selected on the basis of applications submitted by educational organizations. If chosen to host a workshop, the host agency agrees to provide specified facilities and cooperate in the promotion of the workshop. The AIMS Education Foundation supplies workshop materials as well as the travel, housing, and meals for instructors.

AIMS One-Week Perspectives Workshops

Each summer, Fresno Pacific University offers AIMS one-week workshops on its campus in Fresno, California. AIMS Program Directors and highly qualified members of the AIMS National Leadership Network serve as instructors.

The AIMS Instructional Leadership Program

This is an AIMS staff-development program seeking to prepare facilitators for leadership roles in science/math education in their home districts or regions. Upon successful completion of the program, trained facilitators may become members of the AIMS Instructional Leadership Network, qualified to conduct AIMS workshops, teach AIMS in-service courses for college credit, and serve as AIMS consultants. Intensive training is provided in mathematics, science, process and thinking skills, workshop management, and other relevant topics.

College Credit and Grants

Those who participate in workshops may often qualify for college credit. If the workshop takes place on the campus of Fresno Pacific University, that institution may grant appropriate credit. If the workshop takes place off-campus, arrangements can sometimes be made for credit to be granted by another institution. In addition, the applicant's home school district is often willing to grant in-service or professional-development credit. Many educators who participate in AIMS workshops are recipients of various types of educational grants, either local or national. Nationally known foundations and funding agencies have long recognized the value of AIMS mathematics and science workshops to educators. The AIMS Education Foundation encourages educators interested in attending or hosting workshops to explore the possibilities suggested above. Although the Foundation strongly supports such interest, it reminds applicants that they have the primary responsibility for fulfilling *current* requirements.

For current information regarding the programs described above, please complete the following:

Information Request

Please send current information on the items checked:

_____ *Basic Information Packet* on AIMS materials
_____ *AIMS Instructional Leadership Program*
_____ *AIMS One-Week Perspectives* workshops

_____ *A Week with AIMS®* workshops
_____ Hosting information for *A Day with AIMS®* workshops
_____ Hosting information for *A Week with AIMS®* workshops

Name _____ Phone _____

Address _____
             Street   City   State   Zip

We invite you to subscribe to AIMS Magazine

Each issue of the magazine contains a variety of materials useful to educators at all grade levels. Feature articles of lasting value deal with topics such as mathematical or science concepts, curriculum, assessment, the teaching of process skills, and historical background. Several of the latest AIMS math/science investigations are always included, along with their reproducible activity sheets. As needs direct and space allows, various issues contain news of current developments, such as workshop schedules, activities of the AIMS Instructional Leadership Network, and announcements of upcoming publications. *AIMS the Magazine* is published monthly, August through May. Subscriptions are on an annual basis only. A subscription entered at any time will begin with the next issue, but will also include the previous issues of that volume. Readers have preferred this arrangement because articles and activities within an annual volume are often interrelated.

Please note that a subscription automatically includes duplication rights for one school site for all issues included in the subscription. Many schools build cost-effective library resources with their subscriptions.

YES! I am interested in subscribing to AIMS Magazine

Name _____   Home Phone _____

Address _____   City, State, Zip _____

Please send the following volumes (subject to availability):

_____Volume X (1995-96) $5.00			_____Volume XV (2000-01) $35.00			
_____Volume XI (1996-97) $5.00			_____Volume XVI (2001-02) $35.00			
_____Volume XII (1997-98) $5.00			_____Volume XVII (2002-03) $35.00			
_____Volume XIII (1998-99) $5.00			_____Volume XVIII (2003-04) $35.00			
_____Volume XIV (1999-00) $35.00			_____Volume XIX (2004-05) $35.00			

(Note: Prices may change without notice)

Check your method of payment:

☐ Check enclosed in the amount of $_____

☐ Purchase order attached (Please include the P.O.#, the authorizing signature, and position of the authorizing person.)

☐ Credit Card   ☐ Visa   ☐ MasterCard   Amount $ _____

Card # _____   Expiration Date _____

Signature_____   Today's Date _____

Make checks payable to **AIMS Education Foundation**.
Mail to AIMS Magazine, P.O. Box 8120, Fresno, CA 93747-8120.
Phone (559) 255-4094 or (888) 733-2467 FAX (559) 255-6396
AIMS Homepage: http://www.aimsedu.org/

AIMS Program Publications

Actions with Fractions 4-9
Awesome Addition and Super Subtraction 2-3
Bats Incredible! 2-4
Brick Layers 4-9
Brick Layers II 4-9
Chemistry Matters 4-7
Counting on Coins K-2
Cycles of Knowing and Growing 1-3
Crazy about Cotton Book 3-7
Critters K-6
Down to Earth 5-9
Electrical Connections 4-9
Exploring Environments Book K-6
Fabulous Fractions 3-6
Fall into Math and Science K-1
Field Detectives 3-6
Finding Your Bearings 4-9
Floaters and Sinkers 5-9
From Head to Toe 5-9
Fun with Foods 5-9
Glide into Winter with Math & Science K-1
Gravity Rules! Activity Book 5-12
Hardhatting in a Geo-World 3-5
It's About Time K-2
It Must Be A Bird Pre-K-2
Jaw Breakers and Heart Thumpers 3-5
Problem Solving: Just for the Fun of It! 4-9
Looking at Geometry 6-9
Looking at Lines 6-9
Machine Shop 5-9
Magnificent Microworld Adventures 5-9
Marvelous Multiplication and Dazzling Division 4-5
Math + Science, A Solution 5-9
Mostly Magnets 2-8
Movie Math Mania 6-9
Multiplication the Algebra Way 4-8
Off The Wall Science 3-9
Our Wonderful World 5-9
Out of This World 4-8
Overhead and Underfoot 3-5
Paper Square Geometry:
    The Mathematics of Origami
Puzzle Play: 4-8
Pieces and Patterns 5-9

Popping With Power 3-5
Primarily Bears K-6
Primarily Earth K-3
Primarily Physics K-3
Primarily Plants K-3
Proportional Reasoning 6-9
Ray's Reflections 4-8
Sense-Able Science K-1
Soap Films and Bubbles 4-9
Spatial Visualization 4-9
Spills and Ripples 5-12
Spring into Math and Science K-1
The Amazing Circle 4-9
The Budding Botanist 3-6
The Sky's the Limit 5-9
Through the Eyes of the Explorers 5-9
Under Construction K-2
Water Precious Water 2-6
Weather Sense:
    Temperature, Air Pressure, and Wind 4-5
Weather Sense: Moisture 4-5
Winter Wonders K-2

Spanish/English Editions*
Brinca de alegria hacia la Primavera con las
    Matemáticas y Ciencias K-1
Cáete de gusto hacia el Otoño con las
    Matemáticas y Ciencias K-1
Conexiones Eléctricas 4-9
El Botanista Principiante 3-6
Los Cinco Sentidos K-1
Ositos Nada Más K-6
Patine al Invierno con Matemáticas y Ciencias K-1
Piezas y Diseños 5-9
Primariamente Física K-3
Primariamente Plantas K-3
Principalmente Imanes 2-8

*   All Spanish/English Editions include student pages in Spanish and
    teacher and student pages in English.

Spanish Edition
Constructores II: Ingeniería Creativa Con Construcciones LEGO® (4-9)
    The entire book is written in Spanish. English pages not included.

Other Science and Math Publications
Historical Connections in Mathematics, Vol. I 5-9
Historical Connections in Mathematics, Vol. II 5-9
Historical Connections in Mathematics, Vol. III 5-9
Mathematicians are People, Too
Mathematicians are People, Too, Vol. II
Teaching Science with Everyday Things
What's Next, Volume 1, 4-12
What's Next, Volume 2, 4-12
What's Next, Volume 3, 4-12

For further information write to:
AIMS Education Foundation • P.O. Box 8120 • Fresno, California 93747-8120
www.aimsedu.org/ • Fax 559•255•6396

AIMS Duplication Rights Program

AIMS has received many requests from school districts for the purchase of unlimited duplication rights to AIMS materials. In response, the AIMS Education Foundation has formulated the program outlined below. There is a built-in flexibility which, we trust, will provide for those who use AIMS materials extensively to purchase such rights for either individual activities or entire books.

It is the goal of the AIMS Education Foundation to make its materials and programs available at reasonable cost. All income from the sale of publications and duplication rights is used to support AIMS programs; hence, strict adherence to regulations governing duplication is essential. Duplication of AIMS materials beyond limits set by copyright laws and those specified below is strictly forbidden.

Limited Duplication Rights

Any purchaser of an AIMS book may make up to *200 copies* of any activity in that book for use at *one school site*. Beyond that, rights must be purchased according to the appropriate category.

Unlimited Duplication Rights for Single Activities

An individual or school may purchase the right to make an unlimited number of copies of a single activity. The royalty is $5.00 per activity per school site.

Examples: 3 activities x 1 site x $5.00 = $15.00
9 activities x 3 sites x $5.00 = $135.00

Unlimited Duplication Rights for Entire Books

A school or district may purchase the right to make an unlimited number of copies of a single, *specified* book. The royalty is $20.00 per book per school site. This is in addition to the cost of the book.

Examples: 5 books x 1 site x $20.00 = $100.00
12 books x 10 sites x $20.00 = $2400.00

Magazine/Newsletter Duplication Rights

Those who purchase *AIMS®* (magazine)/*Newsletter* are hereby granted permission to make up to 200 copies of any portion of it, provided these copies will be used for educational purposes.

Workshop Instructors' Duplication Rights

Workshop instructors may distribute to registered workshop participants a maximum of 100 copies of any article and/or 100 copies of no more than eight activities, provided these six conditions are met:

1. Since all AIMS activities are based upon the *AIMS Model of Mathematics* and the *AIMS Model of Learning,* leaders must include in their presentations an explanation of these two models.
2. Workshop instructors must relate the AIMS activities presented to these basic explanations of the AIMS philosophy of education.
3. The copyright notice must appear on all materials distributed.
4. Instructors must provide information enabling participants to order books and magazines from the Foundation.
5. Instructors must inform participants of their limited duplication rights as outlined below.
6. Only student pages may be duplicated.

Written permission must be obtained for duplication beyond the limits listed above. Additional royalty payments may be required.

Workshop Participants' Rights

Those enrolled in workshops in which AIMS student activity sheets are distributed may duplicate a maximum of 35 copies or enough to use the lessons one time with one class, whichever is less. Beyond that, rights must be purchased according to the appropriate category.

Application for Duplication Rights

The purchasing agency or individual must clearly specify the following:
1. Name, address, and telephone number
2. Titles of the books for Unlimited Duplication Rights contracts
3. Titles of activities for Unlimited Duplication Rights contracts
4. Names and addresses of school sites for which duplication rights are being purchased.

NOTE: Books to be duplicated must be purchased separately and are not included in the contract for Unlimited Duplication Rights.

The requested duplication rights are automatically authorized when proper payment is received, although a *Certificate of Duplication Rights* will be issued when the application is processed.

Address all correspondence to: **Contract Division**
AIMS Education Foundation
P.O. Box 8120
Fresno, CA 93747-8120

www.AIMSedu.org/
Fax 559•255•6396